Above

Below

A B O V E

ABOVE

BELOW

B E L O W

Text and Illustrations by

C. G. KNOBLOCK

Second Printing

THE BOOK CONCERN
HANCOCK, MICHIGAN
DISTRIBUTORS

COMPOSITION, PRESSWORK AND BINDING BY
THE PLIMPTON PRESS, NORWOOD, MASS.

FOREWORD

From the foredeck of huge automobile ferries gliding smoothly over the straits northward bound, pleasure seeking summer tourists from *below* glimpse for the first time the vast panorama of the land *above*. Soon they will speed over smooth highways to lakes and sparkling waters. Their vacations over, they return reluctantly to their labors *below,* refreshed by brief but invigorating intimacy with nature.

Beyond the park like shoulders of these highways and the trimly painted and decorative efforts of these towns and villages is another world. It lies at the ends of tantalizing trails and logging roads, along unspoiled streams and bays and tiny lakes or in deep silent forests. In it live the people of the north woods, the little people with stout hearts and brave souls. In their lives is dialogue and action the drama of which is witnessed only by those whose privilege it is to live and work and play among them.

That privilege has been mine. This book started as a pastime of impressions and of sketches. It is a pity that in this land of many Deep Harbors, Island Bays and Big Islands, of Hattie Payner and Tom Sanderson, of Indian Pete, of Captain Jim and others, these places and persons exist only in impressions.

To the little people of *above,* to my wife's spirit of helpfulness, human kindness and tender administering of their troubles and their ills, to my daughter Jean who persisted that these sketches and impressions be preserved and who has been so helpful in their composition, this book is dedicated.

The Author

Detour, Michigan
December, 1951

CONTENTS

ABOVE BELOW

HISTORY, adventure, the caprices of Nature and the vagaries of men are very close to that land of great and magnificent distances, the upper Great Lakes country.

In the beginning, geological convulsions in passing millions of years wrinkled the earth's surface, depressing sunken, barren plains, pitching skyward with giant upheavals, rocky escarpments, plateaus, and limitless land areas to form the deep and far-reaching gashes that were later to become the three northernmost of the lakes.

The ice caps followed eons later to apply the inexorable pressure and attrition of erosion, scoring deeply to form the myriads of islands, bays, straits, and headlands, and levelling the sunken plains to form the broad bosoms of vast waters, ageless and limitless.

The slow recession of the glaciers scoured and gouged the surfaces, windrowing the moraines of glacial debris, releasing melting ice and snows, damming the path of new water courses to form thousands of tiny, landlocked lakes, waterfalls, and swamplands.

Then Nature, with artistry unrestrained by convention or consistency of pattern, concealed the hideous harshness of barren uplands with dense and pleasing foliage. And, like a stagehand lighting the props of a fascinating drama, She allowed the sun and sky to reflect upon the backdrop of water and forest in a dazzling contrast of blue, rimmed by a patternless realm of shadowed, delicate greenness.

As if to thwart the commerce that would one day float upon their surface, Nature contrived to elevate one of these lakes above the others and linked it to them with treacherous rapids. As if to taunt the age of man, She placed inestimable mineral and forest treasures beyond this obstacle. As if to retard the northward march of future industry, She fashioned barriers in the form of distracting straits and water courses which for all time he who would travel swiftly on the land must pause to bridge in pursuit of his north or southward courses.

Here commerce and industry, recreation and leisure, law and conservation, social order and education, are but thinly apart from the clinging remnants of frontier pioneering, the attending stupidity and meanness of the human soul, the depravity, corruption, the lawlessness and—the nobility of the individual.

Nor does this gossamer veil conceal the courage and the sincerity of purpose and endeavor of those who, by accident or design, dwell within the encompassing vastness of forests and waters, struggling against barriers they little understand, against forces beyond their comprehension, against the isolation and loneliness of great distances, toward objectives that defy understandable definition. Here is a country of absurd and impulsive contrasts, of human struggle that is always near to, and yet far from, the furious pace of industrialization. Here is a human association that divides thinly the traditions and individualism of the woodsman from the polish, sophistication, and rapture of the urban escapist. Here is a land of scenic grandeur that invites indulgence in its bounty, yet expels intruders with elemental fury. It beckons, yet forbids. It smiles kindly and graciously, yet frowns with ferocious and frightening mien.

Here can be found the tranquility of lovely, inviting landscapes or the depressing harshness of desolation and waste. In the forest fastness and along softly rippling brooks, one can ponder the mystery of deep, quiet pools, yet hear the sound of frightening breakers lashing the rocky shores of limitless seas. Here are inviting trails, offering the safety and delight of close communication with earth, shaded with the darkness of spruce and pine and scented with the tang of balsam and tamarack. Here are the pitfalls and the dangers of pathless forests, impenetrable and forbidding, from whose darkness and deepness emanates an aura of mystery and adventure.

Here are the primitive shelters of the bush, the trim and rugged cabins of the hardy settlers, within the sound and sight of famed resort hostelries. Here are tiny communal centers, lost in the vastness of forest tangle or huddled along remote waterways, some striving with brave hope to improve their lot and fortunes, others content with the squalor, filth, and poverty of primitive isolation, preferring sinful pursuits, lawless endeavor, and a pointless existence.

Here on the connecting water courses, guided through treacherous channels by the most modern of navigational aids, sail the giant, sleek ships of Great Lakes commerce, bringing coal and fuel from the areas *below*, or returning with mineral treasures from the furthermost tip of the greatest of all lakes *above*. Their throaty whistle blasts resound through the dark, mysterious loneliness of the islands and hinterland shore lines where deer and bears and perhaps a lordly moose raise their heads in amazement.

This is a land where time moves from the awfulness of frozen winter waste to a hesitant, uncertain spring, leaving traces of snow and ice and the bitterness of intense cold behind long into the short-lived summer to follow.

And as the days shorten and the fury of the equinoctial storms lash the lakes, visiting upon them destruction, disaster, and fear, autumn comes. Then, as if to atone for the briefness of the summer season, Nature indulges in a colossal spectacle, a pageant of color and beauty, of charm and autumnal sunshine, and of stimulating frosts, and She summons from the northern sky nightly visitations and impressive displays of northern lights, scintillating and ever changing, as the curtain slowly ascends.

Then the leaves fall, the snowshoe hare changes his coat to white, the tamaracks appear naked in the early fading light; over head, the waterfowl from the northern marshes race swiftly southward. The blueness of the open waters fades into a forbidding, steely gray, the straits and water courses bind the islands and the mainland with thick bridges of ice, the headlands appear purple in a backdrop of metallic sky, the last ships pass downward to fairer climes and winter moorings *below*, and winter places a mantle of white over the desolation of leafless forests. Silence and loneliness reign.

Life, its needs, its passions, its tragedies, its sorrows, and its laughter continue.

Before the promising breath of spring again lifts the mantle of silence, many new hopes, new lives, new fears, and new dreams will replace defeat, death, discouragement, and illusion.

This is a big land, and within its forested reaches it encompasses a remarkable diversity of folk. Its communal centers are hamlets far apart, dwarfed by the immensity of space.

Within, life's constant drama unfolds in a succession of spontaneous and unrelated playlets, free from the restraint of propriety and convention, and apart from the exacting relationship of time. Its comedy is more amusing, its tragedy more profound, and its players accept the absurdities of their participation without resentment or complaint.

If one seeks the companionship and hospitality of the rustic woodsman, the trapper, the fisherman, the hunter, or the toiler of the sod, here in this big land his weatherbeaten countenance is commonplace. In many, the signs of racial strains, obscure and remote, indicate national origins that color the interesting and exciting history of the land.

Finnish, Polish, and Italian features reflect the resourcefulness and greed of the early exploiters of the mineral and forest wealth that beckoned onward the advancing outposts of an expanding people. Here also are the remnants of the colonial ambitions of Old World empires, reflecting the early Jesuit influences of France and the military impact of the British. The retreating Redman who roamed the forests and the waters, bewildered by the intrusion of the white race, has also left his mark.

Frenchman, Canadian, Indian—all, by name and deed, have left imprints of their lives, their hopes, and their character.

These are the natives, not in the sense of aboriginal beginnings, but by the accident of history and migration only a few generations remote. It is a sparse population, increasing almost imperceptibly within itself, augmented by newcomers from *below*, newcomers tired and disillusioned, bored by the apparent futility and strife of the concentrated population areas of the motor manufacturing centers.

Thus are blended, by an ever continuing process, the characters and traits, the traditions, philosophies, and the simplicity of the dwellers of a frontier area, with the artificiality and worldiness of urban escapists. Here is found the conflict of contrast, the meeting of guile with cunning, nobility and singleness of purpose with defection and lawlessness.

This is the land of Deep Harbor, of Kettle Island, Island Bay, and Big Island.

This is the land that produced the legendary Paul Bunyan, the less legendary Hattie's boardinghouse, Bullfrog Upton, the Crawfords, Indian Pete, and Beer Suds Joe.

BEER SUDS JOE

THE village of Deep Harbor, though hardly entitled to such an exalted name, was located in the heart of the North Woods. By standards of cities and of other towns and villages, Deep Harbor was exceedingly primitive. It boasted no public sanitation, and even the conveniences of a frontier town were strangers to this ugly collection of houses. But for everything it failed to boast of in the way of the modern appurtenances of less primitive and more forward looking towns and villages, Deep Harbor could point with pride, and often did, to its motley collection of beer halls and taverns.

At one end of its main and only street was the Presbyterian Church. At the other end was a crude but ambitious little Catholic mission. In between these representatives of spiritual hopes and courage were three beer halls and perhaps three hundred of Deep Harbor's citizenry.

Deep Harbor could also boast of about as strange a variety of individuals as might be found anywhere else in the world where the forests have made room for an outpost of civilization. Frenchmen and Finns, Italians and Norwegians, half-breed Indians, Poles, and renegade Welshmen, all mingled together to found a social order which had neither cause for beginning nor reason for continuing to exist. Deep Harbor boasted no leading citizens. Those who would seek civic distinction would necessarily begin at the bottom of the social ladder. If so, they would meet, first of all, Beer Suds Joe.

Night life in Deep Harbor began at sunset. It ended before midnight, not by reason of any observance of government imposed curfews or self imposed restrictions, but by reason of indulgence in excess of capacity, and often of supply, in its favorite beverage, beer. Social life in Deep Harbor moved serenely in an atmosphere of beery aroma and to the delightful tune of gurgling and guzzling and the smacking of lips.

Hugo was the popular barkeeper; he held forth at the Eagle Inn. Next in popularity was Philo, proprietor of the White Tail Tavern. Then followed Jacques; he held forth at the Busy Bee Bar. With all of these, Beer Suds Joe was friendly, and upon this friendship depended his very existence. Joe lived not only by the generosity of these barkeepers, but in addition all the patrons of these social centers were mindful of his welfare. As they lined up at the spacious bars, or sat in crude and slivery booths, the call for refills far exceeded the ability of the lone barkeepers to supply the impatient demand of their guzzling guests. It may never be said that Deep Harbor originated the system of self-service in merchandizing, but it cannot be denied that the generous policy of self-service contributed greatly to the prosperity of the Eagle Inn, the White Tail Tavern, the Busy Bee Bar—

and of Beer Suds Joe. At each end of the bar was a tin bucket into which the self-service guzzlers dumped the dregs of their mugs and bottles as they hurriedly crowded and pushed for refills. As the evening wore on and the crowd became more boisterous, as well as more generous, there could be heard the shouts of "Some more for Joe—fill 'em up—shove the bucket over."

And as the last bleary eyed customer departed on unsteady feet, Hugo or Philo or Jacques as the case might be would wearily gather up the abandoned containers from the bar, the tables, or from the floor and dump the stale remainders into the buckets. After they had counted up the cash in the till, scooped it into a dirty canvas bag, and locked the doors, the social activities and the principal business functions of Deep Harbor would cease.

Beer Suds Joe was conspicuous by his absence in this evening frivolity; his presence never graced the beer halls during the nights. No one knew, nor did anyone care, where Joe spent his evenings, but as surely as the sun would rise in the morning, and long before the barkeepers had slept off the fatigue of an evening of business, he could be seen ambling up the main street with a peculiar, uncertain gait. His clothes were unmistakably hand-me-downs, and much the worse for wear, with evidence that they served not only as street apparel but also as slumber garments. No youngster, probably well in his seventies, Joe never washed his face or combed his hair. He must have had an occasional shave or haircut, for he wore no beard with the exception of his scraggly mustache. He always wore a shirt which once upon a time had been white. His face was tanned and from beneath bushy eyebrows there peered a bright and searching pair of eyes, set wide apart and on either side of a red and conspicuous nose.

The citizens of Deep Harbor appeared to be late sleepers, for, as the sun rose early, the only other signs of life to greet Joe on his morning amblings were a variety of curs and mongrels, who by a generous wagging of tails gave evidence of the deep friendship which existed between their canine interests and this human derelict.

As Joe's steps would bring him to the first beer hall, he would hopefully try the door knob and then resignedly seat himself upon the stoop, waiting for the awakening of the barkeeper. When finally the latch was rattled, Joe would rise quickly for one his age, and acknowledge happily the barkeeper's morning greeting, whereupon he would fall vigorously to his daily task, that of sweeping out the refuse of the bar room. Having finished this expenditure of energy, Joe would await expectantly the recompense of his efforts— the bucket of stale beer left from the night before. His chores thus completed and his stipend received, Joe would take himself to Jacques', and there, having repeated his patient waiting and eventual award, and having done his chore and received his payment, he would amble on to Philo's. All this would require less than an hour of Joe's precious time. With his rounds completed, he would smack his lips and amble out of town. By then, too, the rest of Deep Harbor was beginning to stir into morning life, a life which, day after day, month after month, and year after year, ended in a festivity of beer guzzling and nightly contributions to Joe's sustenance.

The scene described in the foregoing paragraph might have taken place at any time—twenty-five years ago, ten years ago, five years ago, a month ago, or today. It never varied, winter or summer, rain or shine.

But into the life of the village there came, slowly and unmistakably, the consciousness that there was, somewhere in the world, a war. Its cause and objective may have been

vague in the minds of the townsfolk, but month after month
and year after year the young men were disappearing from
the village scene. Not that this diminished or in any way affected Deep Harbor's social quality, but with it came vague
and disturbing indications that the government wanted not
only its young men, but also much money. Under the pressure of the local school teacher, who daily gave the children
pamphlets on the patriotic duty of buying war bonds to be
taken home to their somewhat disinterested parents, some
bonds were indeed purchased, and these largely by the local
barkeepers. And occasionally some of the elders averred
that bonds might be a good investment and reached into the
family sock for what they called a "contribution." Most,
however, claimed abject poverty and, as can be expected,
Deep Harbor as a community broke no records for war bond
purchases.

However, as in all communities, townships, or counties, even in the backward and remote areas, local leadership
would manifest itself in drives and fund raising campaigns
of public interest, not excepting ones for raising money for
the war. And while such a patriotic urge may have escaped
the remoteness of Deep Harbor, it was not lost at the county
governmental level.

And so it came about naturally that the county leadership in its major population center rose to the occasion and
organized its patriotic drive to stimulate the sale of war
bonds. It laid its plans to reach the remote hamlets of the
hinterland, the lumber camps, the fishing settlements, in
fact the very slogan was "Leave No Door Unopened." And
so by boat, canoe, automobile, and by horse and buggy or
on foot, the county drive began. Stunts to draw crowds were
planned and executed. Nightly the leaders gathered together to fire its volunteers with enthusiasm and to plan new

and often ingenious tactics. It hesitated not at all to resort
to the ballyhoo of the County fair or to the artifices of Hol-
lywood deception.

One morning a notice appeared at the local post office,
heralding the visit of a captured German tank and Messer-
schmidt, which would on a subsequent morning be displayed in the interest of increased war bond sales.

It might be said for Deep Harbor that at least the village attended the exhibition, almost to a man. And it so
happened that its timing concurred with Joe's early morning
activities.

Joe stood at the outer rim of the crowd, his shabby coat
bulging as usual with his meager possessions, and watched
the exhibition. A pretty WAC gave the sales talk. An easy
to look at, though obviously spurious, movie actress furnished the scenery. A husky marine did the ballyhooing.

The town listened with rapt attention. So did Joe, his
bright blue eyes peering beyond the redness of his nose.

The husky marine mounted to the seat of his jeep.
"Listen, men, right now there may be boys from your own
village dying in their foxholes. What has Deep Harbor done
to back them up? They need guns—they need ammunition—
they need cannons—and they need airplanes. It's folks like
you that got to supply them by buying bonds and more
bonds. We're here to put your village on the war map, and
to show you that we mean business, we're going to sell at
auction, right this minute, a war bond, and for the man who
buys the biggest bond, the lovely Gloria here will favor him
with a kiss. Who will start the bidding?"

A sort of murmur went through the crowd. Men of
fifty apprehensively looked around to see if their wives
might be there. Joe blinked and also looked about him.
Hugo grinned and looked questioningly at his likely com-

petitor, Jacques. Jacques in turn looked at Philo. Philo looked back at Hugo. Somewhat meekly, Jacques said, "Twenty-five dollars."

Hugo shot back, "Fifty."

His echo had hardly died away when Philo said, "Seventy-five dollars."

Jacques came back with a vociferous "One hundred dollars," and with competition mounting and the bidding going fast, Hugo triumphantly raised his voice with a hopeful shout of "Two hundred dollars."

There came a hush. In Hugo's eye there was a victorious glow. The husky marine, in his best imitation of a country auctioneer, shouted, "Two hundred dollars, I have a bid for two hundred dollars. Who'll make it two hundred and fifty?"

Hugo looked at Jacques; Jacques looked at Philo; Philo peered back at Hugo. By all appearances, Hugo had whipped his competition. The marine was intoning, "Going—going—going. One—two—three . . ."

From the rear of the crowd came a noisy stirring, a jostling and clatter from which emerged the shabby figure of Beer Suds Joe. In a high pitched, wheezy voice, and much to the consternation of the auctioneer, he cried, "Two hunra an' feefty dollas."

The crowd laughed; Joe flushed so much that the rest of his face matched his nose; the townsfolk thought it a good joke. Hugo held his sides in laughter. Jacques grinned and tapped his head. Philo nudged his neighbor with his elbow. The children giggled and the women chuckled.

Again the marine was intoning, "I have two hundred fifty dollars. Who'll make it three hundred? Going—going—going—gone! What is the name of the buyer?"

As Joe hesitated, someone in the crowd shouted oblig-

ingly, "Beer Suds Joe." Joe, meanwhile, was elbowing his
way toward the rostrum. The beautiful movie actress looked
at him apprehensively. Joe fumbled in his pockets, and
from pocket after pocket in his shabby coat and in his trousers and in his shirt, in fact from every possible receptacle of
his belongings, he shelled out onto the pavement nickels,
dimes, half-dollars, dollars, beer bottle caps, and cigarette
butts. The marine laboriously counted out the total, and finally announced receipt of the purchase price of a two hundred and fifty dollar bond.

What happened next has many versions, and remained
the topic of town talk for many a moon. Some said that Joe
reached shyly for his just reward, receiving a most ineffective touch of the lips of the beautiful Gloria. Others talked
loud and long of the vigorous embrace within which Joe
planted his beery lips upon the scarlet ones of the actress.
Whichever way it was, the amazed incredulity of the townsfolk and the shrinking of the enticing beauty can well be
imagined.

Upon the furtive figure of Beer Suds Joe came the halo
of distinction. He was not only the town's leading war bond
buyer, but had also kissed a movie star. In almost every
household that night the menfolk received severe lectures
on conduct and carelessness from their irate spouses. For
many a week thereafter in the activities of the beer guzzling hours, change from payment for Deep Harbor's fa-
vored beverage was carefully placed in deep and sound pockets or change purses, lest the sawdust refuse of the bar room
floors should again yield a fortune to this derelict of distinction.

But not for long. The urgency of war passed on. In the
boisterousness of Deep Harbor's emporiums the tempo of
thirst quenching resumed its vigorous stride. "Dis one's for

Joe" or "Shove the bucket over" could again be heard in
overtones of the otherwise buzzing conversation. And in
the morning when the sun rose, the canine friends of a human derelict wagged their tails kindly as the call came for
the early labors of the ambling Beer Suds Joe.

HERMIT OF THE HARDWOODS

No enchanting origin is attached to the nickname of
Stumpy Shaper, the Hermit of the Hardwoods, nor is the
allusion to his social seclusion an actual characterization of
him. Stumpy lived in a crude hut in a tiny clearing amid
the hardwoods, several hours' walk over dusty trails and
roadways from the village of Deep Harbor. Of leisure he
had plenty, and being by nature relaxed and complacent he
punctuated his frequent trips to the village with restful interludes, during which he would roost upon a convenient
tree stump, of which there were many along the way.
Stumpy's short, stocky stature, short legs, and well upholstered posterior were admirably adapted to find such primitive accommodations comfortable and conducive to pleasant and patient reverie. Hence his name.

Having long been a familiar figure hereabout, carrying
his past in an aura of unknown, and living in the remote hut
in the hardwoods as he did, Stumpy acquired a reputation as
a hermit, erroneous as it may have been. For Stumpy, on
the contrary, loved to talk long and volubly to any one who
would listen and, remote as his habitude may have been,
he welcomed with genuine pleasure and enthusiasm the
few visitors who chanced to stray his way. And they were
very few.

Almost daily Stumpy could be seen in the village. Some times he would saunter in on foot, but more often he would alight from a car or truck, gaily shouting his appreciation for the lift. No doubt the tree stump that gave him restful comfort served not only as a pedestal for reverie, but also as a vantage point from which to beg a ride. In this country of sparse population few would pass by a hitch-hiking gesture, especially when accompanied by the ruddy, smiling countenance of Stumpy Shaper. And few travel this way who have not long since come to know the little hermit. Perhaps this very convenience of conveyance prompted the frequency of his village visits.

Stumpy's purchases were always meager, often as little as a package of cheap tobacco, a pound of nails, or a loaf of bread. Once each month he would cash a check at the local general store. In the twenty odd years that Stumpy had brought this piece of paper, Tom Sanderson steadfastly refused to reveal the amount or source to curious townsfolk. Naturally there was much speculation about this, but the austerity of Stumpy's possessions, the small purchases made, and the careful selection by price would indicate an amount hardly affording more than a low level of subsistence.

Nevertheless, Stumpy's ruddy complexion and well rounded physique would suggest a healthy and substantial diet. This was, no doubt, because he lived off the land, the woods, and the waters, tilling his garden with an eye to self sufficiency and economy. Indeed, Stumpy often boasted of his berries, onions, and cabbages, of his maple syrup and acorn coffee, of his skill in finding and raiding the combs of wild honey, and of his success in his pursuits of fish, beast, and fowl.

In a sense it may be said that Stumpy was abstinent with respect to intoxicating beverages. This was true only to the extent that he never bought a drink. However, he never turned one down. Slight over-indulgence provoked him to song, and always it was a patriotic song, as often sung in French or German as in English. At such times too, Stumpy became very loquacious and paraphrased the subject of his own and others' remarks with ancient parables, adapted, of course, to his own peculiar vocabulary. These parables he spouted off, barely pausing for breath, as he buttonholed the listener closely, his head upturned and barely reaching the other's chest. The listener, breaking away from the near embrace by supreme effort, would often end the verbal avalanche by remarking accusingly, "Stumpy, you have been living on onions again this week."

And Stumpy, lacking a scriptural proverb for a suitable retort, might answer with a somewhat syrupy pronunciation, "Distain not de lowly onion, babies cry for em, women sigh for em."

If any one believed that Stumpy during these garrulous moments might lift the curtain that veiled his seventy odd years, they were doomed to disappointment. With unmatched fluency spiced with pungent backwoods vernacular he would discourse on any subject; but the obscurity of his past he shared with no one. That is, perhaps, with the exception of Betty.

Now to know Stumpy was to know Betty, and the reverse might also be true. What Betty's ancestry lacked in canine respectability, she more than compensated for in affection for her master. The obscurity of her breed matched that of Stumpy's past, and perhaps this was the common denominator that linked them in mutual affection. Stumpy understood Betty and, if vigorous tail wagging and sprightly prancing when addressed was any indication, Betty understood Stumpy. There was no denying the depth of their companionship. Where Stumpy went, so went Betty, except only along the main travelled road. When Stumpy ambled off townward, Betty would accompany him as far as that road. There, hidden in the dense cedars, she would await his return, her big brown eyes patiently expressing a sad anxiety over the separation and an eager anticipation of reunion.

Upon Stumpy's return, Betty would bounce out of hiding and whine in joyous ecstasy. Thereupon he would chide her for her uninhibited conduct, and then launch into an account of his visit to Deep Harbor, omitting not a detail.

From the main road the trail to Stumpy's hideout, as he was wont to call it, wound through dense cedar thickets, skirted deep tamarack swamps, and crossed a delightful brook that gurgled a friendly accompaniment to the soft sighing of the pines lining its moss laden banks. Winter, summer, spring, autumn—no matter what the weather— Stumpy and Betty shared the delight of this hour-long walk unhurried. Always there was the rapt expectancy of flushing a sharp-tailed grouse or fleet snowshoe rabbit from the leafy bowers, or perhaps of seeing the sleek glide of a coyote or glimpsing a lumbering bear, or a white-tailed deer.

It would be along this primitive path under an arch of blue skies supported by the towering green of lovely trees that Stumpy would pour forth to his eager listener tales of his boyhood. He would tell of incidents of his seventy odd years, or confide cherished thoughts, beliefs, and ambitions. In Betty he found the response and respect doubtlessly denied him by the intolerant and often cruelly derisive treatment accorded him by the well meaning but thoughtless folks of Deep Harbor.

The brooklet was the halfway mark, and here Stumpy

and Betty often rested, sprawled on a huge boulder that overhung a deep though tiny pool. Here Stumpy would lie flat and peer into the dark depths to watch the brown trout flitting over the light colored sand bottom and darting into the opaque security of the overhanging grass laden banks, or the less timid rough fish gliding leisurely over the shallows, their tails fanning the soft sand into patterned windrows. Betty would sit back on her haunches, head bowed forward, ears perked in anticipation and doubtlessly in uncomplaining wonderment at her master's eccentricities.

The path followed along the banks of this friendly brook for a quarter of a mile. Then the brook was joined by still another but smaller stream and the path turned abruptly to skirt water impounded behind a beaver dam. Here Stumpy would admonish Betty to silence as they approached a fallen pine, half its roots still nourished by the lifted sod, leaning steeply toward the pond. Its gnarled branches green and pliable, afforded a railing by which they could scale the sloping trunk. From this concealment Stumpy and Betty would watch the beaver colony engaged in the industrious prosecution of family labors, patching the dam and floating succulent softwood to replenish the larder, or lying in contentment upon mud flats, or squatting in shallow waters on sentinel assignment. Betty would sit close to Stumpy on his elevated perch, shivering either over the precariousness of their position or the instinctive urge for the chase.

Always following this restful interlude Stumpy would lecture Betty on the virtues of the noble, industrious beaver and caution against savage canine instincts intending harm to these woodland creatures. Betty would respond characteristically, in apparent understanding of these friendly admonitions.

When they at last reached the clearing they would climb the crude stile of the cedar post fence protectively surrounding the little garden. Stumpy would sit on the top step and address Betty in a companionable but boastful manner. Pointing to his tiny shack he would cry, "Der iss our little hideout."

Then, as if to reflect upon the possible import of his words upon his companion's canine intellect, he would pause. A wagging tail having reassured him, he would continue, "Dis winter we will finish de roof and frame de door and put a glass window in de front, and den our labor for twenty years will be done and finished."

Seeking perhaps to provoke Betty into an expression of possessive delight, Stumpy would then open a package and display his purchase of the day. "See, Betty, I got de hinges and de bolts for de door."

So would end one of many town journeys, and, as Betty would scamper with delight the remaining few yards to the crude shack, Stumpy would bare his head and with dignified formality lower the tattered American flag from the cedar pole erected in front. Preparation of his and Betty's supper would usually be accompanied by a lecture on proper flag protocol, the meaning of the stars and stripes and a discourse on their history.

Somehow one would know Stumpy's shack as belonging to him. Into its crude but substantial construction went some of his personal sturdiness and plainness. Its outward appearance belied its interior. The former lacked any semblance of graceful form, whereas the latter represented an individual desire for simplicity and practicability befitting a lone male occupant. In the center of the single room stood an old wood range serving for both cooking and heating. A platform hung from one wall accommodated a mattress of a sort, with several army blankets, threadbare and faded. A gunny sack filled with balsam needles served for a pillow, and what it lacked in beauty it more than compensated for in its forest fragrance.

A similar platform, also built in and suspended, held a dishpan, a broken soap dish, and a battered water pail. A plain board imbedded in the logs above held a cup, a plate, and a knife, fork, and spoon, and neatly arrayed and hung on wooden pegs were the few cooking utensils that his plain fare required. If there were any provisions they must have been contained in the old canvas bags suspended from the rafters. A single clothes hook, bare of any garments, would indicate that such personal belongings as Stumpy owned he wore, and that it served only for the night.

There was one chair. Its seat, upholstered with a deer hide, and its back, laced with rawhide thongs, attested to a successful attempt to keep in service a furniture item that had long since seen its best days.

At the far end of the room was still another platform built into the wall and strengthened by suspension from the ceiling. On it was stacked a neatly arranged supply of firewood. Over the door a rifle lay on a rack of antlers, accompanied by a corn straw broom and above that, on two long and sturdy pegs, a small steamer trunk whose scarred leather cover spoke of years long past.

That was all. One would first be struck by the meagerness of Stumpy's possessions, then by the practicalness of his home. No one item except the stove and chair rested on the floor. This in itself lent an opportunity for neatness and cleanliness of which the owner quite obviously took full advantage. The walls, floor, ceiling, and platforms were devoid of any semblance of paint, but as spotless as if they were newly planed pine boards. Through the doorway, cov-

ered by a battered canvas tarpaulin when closed, could be
seen a path leading to a mound of earth which was Stumpy's
root cellar. Another path led off to the right to a privy, its
construction so primitive that a cedar branch would have
afforded as much concealment.

If indeed the sum total of this abode required twenty
years of labor, one would wonder what diversions and dis-
tractions or other time consuming pursuits interfered.
No adornments affording graciousness, nor books lending
knowledge, were present; yet the lone occupant spouted po-
etry and history, sang songs, and spoke in parables.

. . .

It was late June, a brilliant summer month pulsing
with forest life and animated color. The clean white bark
of birches, the deep green of cedars, and the bright emerald
of hardwoods framed the grassy clearing of Stumpy's hideout. Young vibrant life everywhere inspired Stumpy to whistle and sing as he fastened the hinges of his newly framed
door. Betty watched him from the shade of a dogwood tree,
her mournful eyes expressing regret that maternal duties
for the moment prevented her from joining her master's exuberance in a prancing, tail wagging accompaniment.

When, however, Stumpy gave one last vigorous blow
with his hand ax and in high spirits yelled, "Der she iss, she
iss done!", Betty could contain herself no longer and sprang
forward to join the celebration. Her squealing pups, hanging
to her fountains of nourishment, dragged with her in ludicrous spills and tumbles, accompanied by complaining yaps
and whines which brought forth a mock rebuke from
Stumpy. Betty, ever sensitive to even mild criticism from
her beloved master, sat back on her haunches and shame-
facedly allowed her offspring to take new holds while she

looked apologetically at Stumpy, her eyes pleading for tolerance of the embarrassing conduct of the puppies. Stumpy
lowered his voice and in kindness said, "Dat's alright, Betty,
you was a pup once."

Then, glancing at the sun, he continued, "Today we
go to Deep Harbor." Betty's relief was unbounded and not
heeding the discomfiture of her suckling brood she leaped
and pranced in unbridled ecstasy.

Having herded the brood into the shack for safekeeping, Stumpy carefully closed the door, latched and locked it,
and said, "See how it works, Betty. Locks don't keep out dis-
honest peeple, but it keeps peeple honest, de pups iss safe
and we go to Deep Harbor."

It was late that sunny summer afternoon when Stumpy
alighted from a truck at the juncture of the trail and the
travelled road on his return from the village. Politely thank-
ing the friendly driver, who was soon lost in the distant dust,
he arranged the burdensome packages for the long walk to
the clearing. Betty bounded out of the thicket with a joyous greeting and together they turned westward and toward
home.

Stumpy paused frequently to rearrange the bulky packages. At every pause Betty ran ahead on the trail, then
turned to look at Stumpy expressing a silent plea for haste
so that she could rejoin her brood. On one of these pauses
Stumpy looked at her speculatively and said, "Now look,
you, I gotta bone for you which iff you carry it we kin git
home faster." And from a paper sack he pulled a huge bone
with remnants of red meat clinging to it. He tossed it to
Betty, who picked it up wagging her gratefulness, in apparent forgiveness and understanding of her master's loitering.
Stumpy rearranging his remaining burdens, and slinging his

sack over his shoulder then proceeded down the forest trail saying, "Now ain't dat better?"

There is something about a man bending under a burden, plodding on his way with directness of purpose, that arouses admiration. It depicts a courageous sense of personal responsibility, of self sufficiency and of attainment. It reveals the instinct for survival in a modern sense, but nevertheless as grim, if not as ruthless, as in more primitive ages. Something of this admiration must have come to the mind of Stumpy as he watched Betty trotting ahead of him. She held her head high with pride and resolution, carrying the meaty bone and pausing now and then to allow for Stumpy's slower progress, exhibiting the while impatience and anxiety.

"Now Betty, dem pups iss alright so don't you hurry so," chided Stumpy.

Then as if to temper her petulance, he launched into an account of his visit to town. "Stumpy spended all hiss money today," he began, and then there followed an enumeration of each purchase, its purpose and its cost, including, of course, the bone for Betty. To all this Betty wagged an understanding acknowledgment, concealing not at all her disappointment as Stumpy threw down his burden to rest himself on the overhanging rock at the brook.

Having filled and lighted his pipe, he leaned back and reflected. Betty meanwhile gave up her entreating glances and, setting the bone on the ground, lay with her nose close to it in readiness to proceed when her master so willed. Stumpy exhaled a cloud of smoke and, more to himself than to Betty, said, "A fool and hiss money don't stay company long." Only a feeble wag greeted this remark.

As if to unburden further troublesome thought,

Stumpy continued, "Next week iss Fort of July, and we git no check till almost de middle of de month." Then rising slowly, much to the pleasure of his impatient companion, he knocked the ashes from his pipe and reached for his sack.

A fleeting glimpse of the red gray of a coyote in the dense foliage ahead caught his eye, and with the agility of a feline he dropped flat on the rock, pinning Betty to the ground with him. The wild creature came into full view some hundred feet from where Stumpy and Betty lay in blended concealment. There it paused, alert and suspicious, and Stumpy noted its full nipples and the rabbit it carried in its mouth. The coyote, apparently satisfied that nothing boded ill, swung into a small arc to the brook somewhat upstream from where Stumpy watched quietly.

The animal trotted stealthily up the stream, paused to survey the terrain, and then walked steeply up the higher bank and entered a concealed crevice between two rocks from which a fresh slash of earth tumbled lightly to the brook below. Suppressing Betty's excited shivering, Stumpy slid noiselessly to the downstream side of the overhanging rock and by a circuitous route joined the homeward trail well out of sound and scent of the coyote.

Not until then did he say anything, but he spoke with excited animation. "Dat wass a she coyote, Betty, with young uns, any how a haff dozen."

Waiting for the import of this remark to sink into Betty's mind, he continued, "Six coyote puppies maybe, one hundra dollars for bounty we get." Glancing at the sun he added, "Too late tonight yet, but come morning we dig dem pups out."

Then with quickened pace, much to Betty's delight, he headed homeward repeating over and over, "Everything comes to him what works hard while he waits."

Having foregone their usual spying on the beaver colony, they soon reached the cedar post fence, only to freeze into horrified immobility at the sight before them.

Where once had stood the crude but homey shack, only a blackened kitchen range remained in abject loneliness in a rim of gray and still smoldering ashes. Slowly Stumpy climbed the stile and, staring in disbelief at the ruin, walked dejectedly and wordlessly toward it. Betty meanwhile raced frantically around the embers, whining pitifully for her lost puppies and glancing pleadingly at her master as if he could give her hopeful assurance.

Against a scarred tree leaned Stumpy's garden spade, and above it his battered woodsman's axe. The root cellar remained unharmed. Kicking the hot embers, Stumpy found his rifle, its stock burned off and its barrel warped by the intensity of the heat, a twisted pail and dishpan, but nothing more. Turning to the flag pole he saw it fallen, its halyard smoking in charred uselessness and the cedar pole crumpled into charcoal brittleness. The tattered flag, miraculously fallen into a muddy spot, was soiled but unharmed. Tenderly he gathered it up, cut it from the smoldering rope, and walked dazedly to the stile. Betty followed whimpering.

As Stumpy sat down on the lower step he sighed, "Twenty years hard labor gone by de stroke of fate, we got no money, we got no check, we got no food and we got no place to sleep." Then patting his sorrowful companion gently, he added, "We got our root cellar, a spade, and a ax and," pausing he looked down on the soiled flag, "and Old Glory."

Early the next morning, having somehow survived a homeless night, Stumpy with his spade on his shoulder, resignation to fate in his ruddy face, and the courage to begin again in his heart, proceeded rapidly up the stream bed. Beside him trotted Betty, equally resigned and doubtlessly as courageous, wondering perhaps at the unusual briskness of his gait. Reaching the coyote den, Stumpy stooped and looked at the telltale tracks. "The big she coyote iss gone out huntin'—now we git dem pups—and maybe a hundra dollars."

While he sat down for a smoke before proceeding with his labors, Betty started to dig frantically into the soft earth inside the crevice, barking her enthusiasm. Stumpy continued smoking, apparently in deep thought, and staring at the ineffectiveness of Betty's efforts.

As if coming to a momentous decision, he rose suddenly, viciously knocked the ashes from his pipe, and yelled, "Leave it alone, you, Betty!"

Startled by the unaccustomed severity of the command, Betty paused and, turning her head toward her master, shrank into quivering, dejected obedience. Stumpy, sensing her obvious discomfiture, continued in a stern though kindlier tone. "You shoulda be ashamed—yesterday you bring home a meat bone to de pups and no pups." He paused to let the words sink in, then continued, "Now you dig up dem coyote pups—what you tink that big she tink when she come home wid a rabbit and find Stumpy and Betty dug em up for one hundra dollar bounty?"

Without further words, he picked up his spade and headed homeward, with Betty following meekly and in disappointment.

The next few days were busy ones for Stumpy and his companion in adversity. Poles and logs were dragged from the forest, peeled and braced to form a crude lean-to. Nails were salvaged from the ashes, laboriously straightened and reused. Hinges were reclaimed, and battered utensils scraped and shaped. The old iron range was propped on field stone neatly arranged to replace its fire weakened legs. There was no money for these needed appurtenances, important even to a most primitive living standard. Nor was there money for food which meant time lost in pursuit of small game and fish and berries. There was no time for trips to Deep Harbor, nor need to go because of straitened circumstances. Pride and independence precluded social calls which might move the rough but sympathetic folks of the village to offer discarded articles or help in other ways. Until the middle of the month brought the expected check, Stumpy would need to improvise or do without and it pleased him that he was getting along so well.

Time sped quickly, all too quickly, and by the time the logs were chinked and the roof patched with birch bark strips to make it raintight, he was reminded that the Fourth of July was tomorrow. He and Betty roamed the cedar swamp to find a pole. It had to be a very special pole, slim, straight, and tall. When he had it erected in front of the lean-to, he stood back and admired his handiwork, boasting the while to Betty attentively watching. Then his face clouded and he walked slow and in deep thought to the fence stile. Wearily sitting on the lower step, he brooded in silence, Betty meanwhile whining her anxiety over the sudden change in her master's spirits. As suddenly his mind seemed to have reached a conclusion and he climbed the stile and walked rapidly up the trail to the distant highway.

That evening was the evening before Independence Day. It had been a busy one in Tom Sanderson's general store. Stumpy had idled about most of the afternoon ill at ease and in apparent uncertainty. Tom, knowing well the buying habits of the little hermit, paid him no heed. When it came time to close up for supper, however, and the last customer had left, he turned to Stumpy inquiringly.

Embarrassed, Stumpy glanced furtively around to make certain no others were there to hear, walked up close to Tom and, turning his face upward with wistful earnestness said softly, abated excitement in his voice, "Mister Sanderson, I got no money till de middle of de month. Kin I buy feefty feet clothesline and pay you when I git my check?"

Tom, reaching for a hank of suitable rope, said laughingly, "Sure, Stumpy, but what in hell you buying rope for? Goin' to hang someone?"

Stumpy reached happily for his purchase. "No, Mister Sanderson, tomorrow iss Fort of July and I need a halyard for Old Glory."

CAPTAIN JIM

PRIVATE JAMES ROSS, member of Company C, First Battalion, 325th Infantry, A.E.F., cupped the dice in his palms, whispered sweet nothings to them, and gently rolled the ivory cubes alongside his last ten franc note on the hard packed dirt floor. "Busted," he said cheerfully and, rising, he dusted the dirt from his breeches and joined his buddy in the corner of the lanternlit stable. Private Benjamin Cohen, member of the same military unit, moved over to make room for him on the straw and asked, "Where do we go from here, Jim?"

"Don't know," grunted Jim, then, wriggling his short, slender body into a heap of straw, he dropped into untroubled sleep. Ben, resigned to the probability that no weighty decisions would be made this night, joined him in slumber.

A fortnight ago Jim and Ben had made a killing with their "ivory providers," as they lovingly called their slightly loaded dice. It had been payday and the first payday after Kaiser Wilhelm's abdication and the resulting armistice of World War I had relieved them of the rigid discipline of combat duty. Unfortunately, one victim had detected the trickery in the dancing ivories. This had caused no end of mortification, due to the need for disposing of the evidence. But they had accomplished this by tossing the profitable cubes into the River Marne, turbulent from November rains. Their momentary opulence had made them fair game for their fleeced doughboy buddies in the matter of small loans, unsecured of course, but expedient under blackmail pressure. Their personal health and wealth had suggested a change, by transfer or furlough or extended leave—in fact by any means that would insure distance between themselves and Company C. Plans for demobilization had ruled out any notion of transfer, and their personal records, cluttered with "confinement to quarters," "kitchen police" assignments, "inspection failures," and at least one guardhouse sojourn had precluded any favorable consideration from shavetail superiors in the way of leaves or furloughs. There was one way out, however, that circumvented all bureaucratic red tape and regulations, and that was to go AWOL. And they had done just that.

Like a pair of well-heeled American postwar tourists, Jim and Ben had taken in Lyons, Avignon, Cannes, and Marseilles, their American army uniforms being their passports to the wine cellars and festive tables of the good folks who hailed them as their liberators. Their prodigious appetites for French wines, and American liquor and the company of mademoiselles of mercenary leanings had made deep inroads into their ill-gotten cash reserves. They had bolstered this by frequent indulgence in crap contests, being careful to play with poilus only. Fearful of gendarme displeasure, they had played with honest dice, but with practiced partnership technique resulting in moderate profit. Travelling without official passes, they had avoided the military police of larger control centers in favor of small villages and towns or suburban areas. They had slept in barns, in cellars, in railway stations or in the superb comfort of white sheets and quilts in the guest rooms of generous and grateful hosts. Wherever they laid their heads at night, they had slept carefree and happy and tired. And now they were broke on a pallet of straw in a stable of a tiny village. They cared not where, and what tomorrow might bring worried them less.

Morning gray streaked through the wide cracks of the clapboard barn when Jim awakened to the restless stomping and munching of horses. Sitting bolt upright, he nudged Ben into wakefulness with a cheerful "Come on, Ben, time has come when we must all mingle together again!"

Ben raised his head. "Where we at?" he inquired sleepily.

"After losing all our dough to dem pirates last night, where do you spose we are," was Jim's reply.

Ben turned over on his face and, stretching his limbs luxuriously, answered, "Don't know, but it smells like a manure pile to me. Where do we go from here?"

Jim looked at his partner. "Why you saphead, we're going to get us some breakfast, then we're going to set us down on the military road and wait until a couple of nice guys with a blue band on their arm which sez military police comes along in a nice army truck and gives us a ride."

"How you goin' to get breakfast without francs?"

"You just follow me," replied Jim.

They found a well pump behind the barn; then, seeing a white pillowcase fluttering from a clothesline, Jim purloined it and they both proceeded with their morning toilet. A short time later, two woebegone American soldiers, one wearing his arm in a soiled white sling and leaning heavily upon his attentive buddy, knocked at the door of a peasant house. A buxom housewife, with pitying solicitude which quickly overcame their language barrier, was soon hovering over the breakfast table, plying them with steaming platters, and clucking sympathetic phrases unintelligible in words, but meaningful in expression.

Breakfast attended to, the blissful pair sauntered down the road. When out of sight of their sympathetic benefactress, Jim tossed the pillowcase behind a clump of trees. Reaching the high road, they chose a comfortable spot to sit and await the inevitable truck ride and with it apprehension as violators of rigid military law.

A few days later, Jim and Ben lounged in well fed and unabashed indolence in the comfortable warmth of the guardhouse barracks behind a chicken wire barrier to freedom. Ben was searching his memory in an attempt to record on a writing paper tablet the hundred odd verses of that ribald but popular tune, "Mademoiselle from Armentières," to take home to the folks in New York and have fun with, as he aptly expressed it. Jim, disdainful of any such cultural efforts, sought in every way to distract him and had some success. After evading answer for the fourth time to Jim's "Whatcha gonna do when you git out of this man's army," Ben tossed the pencil and tablet under his bunk and somewhat scornfully replied, "Goin' in business with my old man."

"What business?" prodded Jim.

"My old man's got a clothing store," Ben replied and, sensing that Jim would not be satisfied except with detailed elaboration, he continued, "it's over in Brooklyn—men's clothes, dress and woik clothes, shoes too, and hats—belongs to the family—my old man wants I should be a clerk so I can take over when he croaks, see?"

As he adjusted his spare blankets into a chaise longue effect in his semi-reclining languor, Jim replied, "Sounds like a hell of a business."

"Oh yeah? So maybe you got better ideas, what you gonna do when you git back to the states, fly kites?"

Jim raised himself on one elbow. "So you're goin' to sell clothes in Brooklyn and the old man croaks and you git the store and then you'll marry some dame that talks Brooklynese and raise a big family of kids and bye and bye wait for the oldest kid to come back from some war and then he works in the store so that when you croak he can get the store—that's a hell of a life."

Warming up to his subject, Jim sat upright. "Look," he said, "I'm going back to the woods where there's lakes and rivers and lots of room—I'm going to build me a boat that's forty feet long with a twelve foot beam with a gasoline engine, a pilot house, and lots of deck space. Summers I'll take city sports out on fishin' parties. I'll get me some nets and sell fish, and I'll carry freight and cedar posts and lumber and anything I can make money on. And winters I'll trap, cut timber, and hunt and have me a good time."

Jim rose to full height and with bumptious dignity he added, "Shake hands with Captain James Ross of the good ship *Islander* hailing from Deep Harbor."

.   .   .

The daily train from *below* clanked to a stop at its terminus in Channel City. It was a raw March day that greeted Jim as he alighted to view again the familiar scenes of his homeland. No committee was on hand to welcome this returning soldier, people having tired by now of the fanfare that had accompanied earlier demobilization.

Shouldering his duffle bag, he sauntered unhurriedly

to the business district. It was noon, and he was soon
perched on a high stool at a lunch counter. As he was wiping up the remaining gravy with a chunk of bread, a booming voice accompanied a slap on his back with "When the
hell did you get in, Jim?" For the first time in nearly two
years, Jim saw a familiar face.

All thoughts of a speedy return to Deep Harbor vanished in the ensuing festivities. It mattered not that he
missed the mail truck that day, nor the next. Considerate
police lodged him behind bars at night for safekeeping and
fed him nourishing breakfasts upon his release in the morning. On the third day, broke but happy and carefree, he
climbed on the truck beside the driver and was soon chat-
tering volubly on his overseas experiences and his big plans
for when he settled down in Deep Harbor.

As Jim alighted at the local post office and general
store, old friends surrounded him with rough but genuine
warmth and friendliness. No distracting incidents, however, interfered with his reaching the unpainted clapboard
cabin where his mother made haste to prepare for her returning son his favorite meal, the while beaming with delight at his unexpected arrival. Neighbors streamed in to
add their greetings and Jim, between huge mouthfuls of
succulent stew and dumplings, delighted his visitors with
tales of Château-Thierry, Saint-Mihiel, and Belleau Wood,
his affairs with Frenchwomen, and his encounters with military police. While his mother looked proudly upon the
gold service chevrons on his left sleeve, Jim expanded with
great exaggeration on the incidents that had awarded him
the single gold chevron on his right. The folks laughed
loudly at his mimicry of French poilus and the boastful allusions to his fighting qualities as a soldier and his artistry
in affairs of the heart.

That evening he was to repeat in boisterous celebration at Hugo's, Jacques', and Philo's his fighting as well as amorous experiences. The early hours of the morning found him wending his way homeward with uncertainty, but basking in the delight of popular adulation and attention.

Popular acclaim for a returning hero has breadth but little depth and a disconcerting inclination to subside into the forgotten past. Private James Ross soon became "that Ross kid" and, free of the distracting admiration of neighbors and friends, Jim turned his thoughts to the coveted acquisition of his dream boat *Islander* and the title of Captain James Ross. He prosecuted the pursuit of these ambitions in the same manner in which he lived—unhurried, unworried, and boldly optimistic.

After a few weeks of loafing, Jim announced at breakfast one morning, "Guess I'll trap beaver next week—pelts are bringing good money and maybe I can buy some oak plank and start my boat." The next few days were spent in making the rounds of old friends, borrowing traps, and visiting beaver ponds for likely locations for his quest. His luck prevailed, and several weeks later at Fairbanks a fur buyer stalked around the offerings of the local trappers and Jim's six hooped pelts brought a tidy sum. Before returning to Deep Harbor, he purchased a useless kitchen gadget for his mother, a frilly jacket for his sister, and a bottle of liquor for himself.

That night Jim repaid his host of friends for their kindness and generosity during his home-coming celebration and, unmindful of his dwindling cash, he paused at Deep Harbor's three beer halls to treat the crowd. The next morning he walked to McConnel's sawmill and critically examined oak logs for planking. The down payment took all his

remaining cash, and his promise to pay the balance when
the logs were sawed was optimistic and enthusiastic.

It took a summer and fall of odd jobs to complete the
payments. By the time he had stored the lumber in his
mother's back yard, the first snows of winter had sent him
to the cozy comfort of the parlor stove. "Too cold to mon-
key at boat buildin'—come spring I'll lay the keel" was his
explanation for the delicious indolence that possessed his
waking hours during the early winter months. In January he
got a job driving a log team. The need for bolstering his
mother's scant means, and the expense of good fellowship
in the village bars left little of his wages. When spring arrived, he took a job as a deck hand on a lumber schooner.

Sailing wages were high and the opportunities for
spending were infrequent. By the time fall storms drove
small craft from the treachery of high winds and pounding
seas, Jim had achieved a degree of opulence that survived
even the festivity of his home-coming after a season of
sailing.

Fall lingered long and Jim busied himself with building a cradle and hewing and splicing the keel of his boat. By
the time winter asserted its icy reign, the *Islander's* newly
hewn keel and curving ribs lay in its cradle, a skeleton of
the ship to be in a bed of fresh shavings and white chips.

Spring followed another winter of comfort and indolence in front of the glowing warmth of the big heating
stove. By the time the tender green of new buds and sprouting grass had sprinkled the deep blue and purple of tree
studded shore lines in a pleasing blend of woodland makeup,
Jim's fancies, as young men's are wont to do, turned to
thoughts of love. While weeds sprouted around the skeleton of the *Islander*, Jim married, and the grave responsibili-
ties of this blissful arrangement drove him in quest of a job

with wages, a move toward security and comfort which left for the time no room for daydreams and nautical ambitions.

So it was to be that year and the years following. The skeleton of the *Islander* took on the dark gray of aging timber, its neglect hidden by the tall weeds and sprouting poplar. Jim worked where and when work was available. He drove the mail truck, logged on occasion, hired out as a deck hand, or performed menial tasks of infrequent opportunity and questionable income. When he had the time to work at his dream boat, some distraction claimed his fancy, or fishing was too good, or the weather was not good enough, or the time was not propitious. When for the moment he had extra jingling money in his pockets, he would buy nautical gadgets, hardware, or other marine gear. If boats were built of words, the *Islander* would long since have sailed over the deep blue of the straits and the big lake below. Jim's bar room conversations centered upon the attributes of the craft in the making. Already in his mind's eye the *Islander* was carving its name in the commerce of the waterways and sailing boldly on horizons of optimism. Already he was Captain Jim to his cronies.

The world at large talked of the "crash" in terms vague to the good folks of Deep Harbor, and certainly meaningless to Jim. Whatever the impact upon the nation of the 1929 stock market descent, it crept slowly, imperceptibly upon the tiny hamlet.

While the country reeled uncertainly in an ever deepening chasm of economic chaos, spring came as usual to Deep Harbor with the first crashing breakup of the heavy ice on the bosom of the straits. The menfolk awaited anxiously the call to return to sailing jobs, but they waited in vain. Elsewhere, civic leadership asserted itself in clumsy but courageous efforts to stem the engulfing tide, but in Deep Harbor, leaderless, inept, and impotent, full realization came only as the giant ore carrier fleet, always so welcome and abundant on the distant horizon, shrank to a tiny shadow of its once magnificent commerce. As Deep Harbor's primitive economy, never far above depression level and always geared to chance, caprice, and the vagaries of the seasons, halted to collapse, odd jobs and opportunities for gainful pursuit faded into an ignoble void. The approach of summer brought no horde of summer colonists and no eager vacationers from *below*, and the well of the always sparse money income of this hapless village stood withered and dry and hopeless.

Jim, lighthearted and optimistic as usual, heralded the situation with his characteristic philosophy. "Shucks," he said, "I'll git time to finish that boat now."

During the next few months, Jim amazed his friends, his careworn wife, and himself with his industry. Pausing only long enough to replenish the family larder by brief expeditions after woodland game or setting nets for fish, he applied himself vigorously to the neglected *Islander*. By midsummer she slid gracefully, if somewhat prematurely, into the back bay waters of the straits, her new paint glistening in the bright warm sun, her name scrawled crudely but boldly on her bow and stern. Deckless and without pilot house or engine, the hull floated trim and shipshape in contrast to the haunting spectacle of ghostly keel and curving ribs half hidden by weeds and brush.

It was to be early fall before Jim managed to negotiate the purchase of a second-hand engine, shaft, and wheel. Having no cash, he gave a mortgage on the craft. As equinoctial storms lashed the seas, the *Islander's* open hull slashed through the rolling backwater of the stormy lake below on her trial run. Jim, throughly soaked and dripping from the flying spray, but pleased with the admiring glances of his fellow townsmen, brought her into her dock.

The celebration at Philo's, Hugo's, and Jacques' that evening fitted the importance of the occasion. Captain Jim sat on the bar, his feet dangling, and boasted loudly of his sturdy craft, her speed, and her ability to take the heavy seas. Someone asked about her deck and pilot house, to which Jim replied in high good humor, "Aw shucks, I kin git the deck on in no time, and I know where there's an old fish boat beached with deck house good as new. I'll git it and in a week youse guys kin come over and see the swellest damn pilot house on any boat her size in this bloomin' country."

But it was not to be in a week, or two or three. Jim loved his new plaything and the deck and pilot house had to wait while he sailed for the sheer fun of it up and down the straits and among the islands. His credit for gasoline soon ran out and the *Islander* stayed moored to her crude but substantial dock.

Frosty nights signalled the winter to come. It would be a harsh one for the poverty stricken folks of Deep Harbor. In the world outside could be heard the favorite phrases of the time—relief projects, the bonus march, prohibition, Al Capone, liquor syndicates, bootlegging rackets, hijacking —and the mutterings and restlessness of the unemployed. Deep Harbor could not escape the backwash of the depressing affliction that was searing the industrial and agricultural areas *below*. Nor could Jim.

Without deck or pilot house and without running lights the *Islander* would glide out of her mooring berth in the late afternoon and, in the lowering winter sun's feeble light, she would disappear among the islands of the distant bay; but morning would find her moored and shipshape at her Deep Harbor berth. If the townsfolk wondered about the strange nocturnal excursions, they voiced no speculations. Jim, on the other hand, began to show outward signs of some prosperity, his gasoline credit was restored, and new gadgets appeared on his dream boat. Piloting an open boat in the chilling rawness of November nights is at best a cruel and painful experience. Jim's face took on the weather beaten quality of the seafaring fraternity. With lighthearted gayety and cheerful optimism he purchased matched lumber for his decking and mounted his purloined pilot house. By the time these appurtenances had received their coats of protective paint, the heavy, oily roll of the harbor backwaters warned of the ice that would soon seal the bosom of the lakes.

One morning Jim found the *Islander* fast in firm blue ice. Carefully he plugged her seacocks with heavy grease, battened her doors and windows, and moored her with secure and solid lines. That night, almost twelve years to the day of the AWOL junket in the heart of Europe with his army pal, Benjamin Cohen, he sat down and scrawled a letter.

Most of it related to his boat. "She's a honey," he wrote. There followed a description of her characteristics, speed and ability to take the sea. "Been making purdy good money running booze from Canada for some folks down state," he continued, "and next spring I'm going to take her on fish excursions with paying passengers." Concerning his family situation, he wrote, "I got two boys, one nine and one ten, no girls yet, but there is hope." Jim ended his letter with a sly reference to Ben's inferior status as a businessman: "How goes the clothing business, no good, eh?"

Spring came. With it came unforeseen troubles for Captain Jim. Having neglected to pay for the secondhand engine he had purchased by mortgaging his boat, the sheriff served a summons on him and tacked a writ of attachment on the *Islander*. It was some months before Jim raised the money to regain the use of his boat and by that time rum-running had gone under such rigid surveillance that a shift of operating technique was necessary.

The passenger business failed to develop, so Jim bought nets and sought thereby to gain some income. However, not having acquainted himself thoroughly with the rules and regulations that protected the rather sizeable fishing commerce, he ran afoul of the law often enough to absorb not only his profits, but also the payments he should have been making on his nets.

He shrugged this off with his usual lightheartedness by shifting his activities over the international boundary, only to run into border patrol troubles which cost him his fishing nets. "Aw shucks, I'll git me a job floatin' cedar posts" was his optimistic reply to adversity, and he did.

Hauling cedar posts was not a profitable undertaking, first because of Jim's inaccuracy in figuring his expenses, secondly because of the long wait for payment, and last, but by no means least, because of his bland disregard for the rules of navigation. He learned the hard way. One day a coast guard officer visited his boat and to Jim, who was puttering around patching and scraping the hull, he inquired about papers for the boat.

"Papers," exclaimed Jim, "what papers?"

The officer explained patiently that one does not just build a boat, give it a name, and float it on the waters. Documents were required, obtainable at the Customs office, which were renewable at stated intervals.

All this puzzled Jim no end, and since it looked like a complicated and wholly needless procedure, he kept putting it off. He didn't like thinking about complicated matters; it interfered too much with his carefree spirit.

After a summer of profitless boat operation, interrupted by occasional opportunities for wage work, Jim managed to obtain a profitable haulage job on some minor development on a distant island. Unfortunately, his course coincided for a considerable distance with the channels of the big ore carriers. The consequent difficulties of navigation caused him no concern, but apparently it did the masters of these large vessels. Documented or not, the little craft *Islander* was entered into the log books of more than one of the haughty ships, and because in most cases they were incidents of such utter disregard of rules and safety regulations, the authorities of this complicated marine commerce took note.

Swashbuckling unconcernedly down the wrong channel of the otherwise well regulated sea lanes one late summer day, Jim sat on the back shelf of his pilot house, in a half reclining position. His feet were entwined in the spokes of the wheel in a haphazard effort to hold his course, while he leaned back in comfort, pipe in mouth, hands supporting the back of his head—a picture of indolence. The *Islander* danced along at a lively clip, rolling gracefully over the foaming wake of passing ships.

A huge ore carrier, travelling light, her bow haughty and high, with rudder at a quarter port, was making the turn. Jim took only a languid interest in her maneuver which at best was difficult for a six hundred foot hull. The deep throated blast of the danger signal brought Jim to his feet. He had only a fraction of a second to bring his wheel hard over right to escape the dangerous suction of the ship's wheel. As his stern fender grazed the steel hull lightly and the *Islander* responded to her rudder, Jim put his head out the pilot house window and, shaking his fist at the receding monster, yelled, "Where the hell you think you're goin'—want the whole lake to yourself?"

Unfortunately for Jim, but perhaps fortunately for the safety and peace of mind of all the lake captains, a coast guard picket boat happened to be nearby. Hearing the danger signals, it hove to to investigate. Passing the *Islander* on her starboard side, it swung in a great arc to come within hailing distance. To the officer's crisp "Ship ahoy," Jim opened the door and twiddled his nose at him. Always lively at repartee, Jim welcomed the opportunity to exchange banter with the law.

But the picket boat's response to this indignity was not as expected. It throttled its speed to match that of the slower moving *Islander* and, staying abreast a hundred feet out, staged a wordless escort of the offending craft.

It was an uncomfortable two hour period before Jim arrived near his docking berth, with the picket boat paying no heed to him, but pacing him relentlessly instead. As Jim swung to enter his berth he would need to cross the bow of the picket boat or slow down to pass her astern. He decided he would have some fun by scaring the daylights out of the crew and opened his throttle. As the *Islander* leaped to her power, the picket boat flashed across her bow. Out-maneuvered and embarrassed, Jim kept his eyes straight on his course to his dock line. It was not until he had thrown his bowline on the tiny capstan that he dared to look back at his unwelcome escort. The picket boat was close at his stern, and its officers were already setting foot on the dock. The deadly earnestness of their carriage knocked a big dent into his traditional armor of optimism. In an effort to appear nonchalant, Jim busied himself with mooring the *Island-er's* stern and bow, hoping that the uniformed officers were, after all, only paying Deep Harbor a social call. It was not to be.

It took many trips to Channel City that fall for Jim to extricate himself from this maritime offense. The experience was also a thorough primer in navigating rules and regulations. When he was finally dismissed from further interrogation, hearings, contempt citations, and examinations, the blue ice of the straits had closed the inviting waters. And it took several brisk evenings in the bar rooms before he recovered his aplomb; there he found an attentive audience to listen enraptured and amused as he mimicked the sternness of the examining officers and told how he had outwitted them at their own game. "Aw shucks," he said, "them guys ain't so tough—they only dress that way."

During the long winter he lounged comfortably near the kitchen stove. With the arrival of spring there would be the problem of properly documenting his boat, of changing her gear and rigging to comply with established laws and practices, of taking examinations for his pilot's license, and of memorizing pilots' rules and regulations. But why worry about needs that were so many snowstorms and frosty months away?

At Christmas, which was a bleak and dreary one for the villagers and also for Jim's family, he received a post card from his army pal. The clothing business was lousy, it said, and Ben too had a family, a boy ten and a girl nine. "Just think of that lunkhead in that kind of business," Jim said as he tossed the card in the fire.

The *Islander* made a dozen trips that following season before Jim was reminded of the legal preliminaries to engagement in sailing a commercial boat. "Ain't got time to bother with that bunk," was his usual answer when his cronies inquired about progress in that respect. The reminder came when, as he was towing some stray logs from a broken log boom, a picket boat passed by and returned to circle him in critical examination.

Boarding the truck for Channel City the next morning, Jim set about taking care of this unfinished business. The Customs officer explained the contents of a long and complicated document to him which he was to fill out. Jim, not knowing the answers to such inane questions as "gross tonnage," "net tonnage," "load line," "specifications," "draft," "hailing port," and so forth, decided that it would be advisable to take this thing home with him and study it there. The net result of the perplexing questionnaire was that he chucked it in the kitchen cupboard and did nothing about it. His unread pilots' rules and regulations reposed in this same handy whatnot.

The next ten years were to be years of revolutionary change. Deep Harbor rocked gently and ignominiously in the remote backwash of such veiled philosophies as the New Deal, Banking holidays, CCC, PWA, the Blue Eagle, WPA, and a host of political and economic stimulants. The *Islander* remained as before, a craft without documentation. Jim plunged with optimistic abandon into illegal ventures in which his little boat brought at times profit and again losses, and frequent brushes with the law. There were times when the *Islander*, idle and unkempt, chafed at her moorings at Deep Harbor. Then there were periods when she danced on sparkling seas flitting hither and yon on journeys of profit and of fun. Jim took to beachcombing and miscellaneous haulage, the repeal of prohibition having removed the best source of profit.

From foreign lands came rumblings and saber rattling and the folks of Deep Harbor heard of Franco, Hitler, and Mussolini, of Nazism and Fascism, of Communism and Molotov, of Stalin and Chamberlain. However portentous and meaningful the crackling news may have been, Deep Harbor remained as always, a tiny backwoods hamlet nestled in the deep green and brown of its forest fastness, fronting the sparkling straits and the dark headlands of the islands.

The winter following the first Hitler march, Jim sat down and wrote to Ben Cohen. He told briefly of his boys in the CCC camp and dwelt at length upon his boat. "Mama died last fall so it's only me and the boys now," the letter stated and then ended characteristically with "How you doing in the clothing business? Lousy I bet." Thoughtfully Jim added a postscript: "I got a barometer on the boat now and a compass."

Came Pearl Harbor. The land *above below* could not escape the quickened pulse of a nation girding for total war. From the remote areas of Big Island and the ramshackle dreariness of Deep Harbor the young men departed for distant camps; those of military age donned uniforms, while the older men departed for the munitions centers *below*. The woods and waters stirred in response to the throes of warfare and Jim, with his wrinkled, weather beaten countenance from which neither tragedy nor adversity could erase the good humor, spruced up his *Islander* for action.

These would be turbulent years, years in which the *Islander* would plow through the breaking ice floes of springtime and roll in the vicious darkening seas and early blizzards of the approaching winters to perform her contribution to a nation at war. Pulpwood, cedar posts, and lumber would be transported on her sturdy decks. She would respond to her master's gaiety and recklessness and, when at last the freezing spray whipped her combing into glassy whiteness, and her mooring lines froze into ungainly stiffness, Jim would bring her into her home berth, tie her securely to her capstans and, before leaving her to her winter idleness, address her affectionately with, "Be a good girl now—come spring I'll get you a document and me a pilot's license."

During one of these years he kept his promise. Border patrols, more alert and numerous, yet appreciating the need for watercraft and licensed seamen, prevailed upon Jim's neglectful temporizing, and early the following summer Jim bought a watertight tube into which he carefully thrust his vessel's document. Then, buying a cheap picture frame, he carefully mounted his pilot's license and fastened it in his pilot house. In a larger frame he placed conspicuously the pilots' rules of navigation.

The fresh summer's paint on the *Islander's* hull had hardly dried when Jim became ill. All that summer and fall he spent convalescing, at times sitting on the deck of the dormant *Islander* or on the stoop before Hugo's beer hall. If inactivity saddened him, or if the events of these fateful years had undermined his cheerful outlook, it was not evident in his natural repartee. When friends asked him how he felt his reply was quick and witty. "Shucks, never felt better in my life—another month I'll be good as new and me and the *Islander*'ll be chasing them steamboats all the way to Channel City."

That was the summer of world shaking events. The German war machine flopped into dissolution and Hiroshima flattened under the impact of scientific warfare. The following Christmas, Jim received a post card from Ben. Its salutation was brief, its contents just as brief: "My daughter got married, my wife died, and my boy got killed in the war. I'm going to quit the clothing business and got the store up for sale."

Jim answered without his characteristic delay. He wrote a long letter, dwelling mostly on his boat. Of his illness he said little. "Too bad about your wife and boy," he wrote and then, as though adding an unimportant news item, he continued, "My oldest boy went down in the Pacific—my youngest got killed in Germany." No elaboration, no remorse, no bitterness entered the terse statement of fact. Jim ended his letter with "Now Ben, you come out here this summer, we'll go places on the *Islander*, she's a honey of a boat."

Willing and sympathetic hands helped Jim that winter to recondition the *Islander*. The old engine needed complete renewal, and to this end Jim's friends contributed generously of both labor and material. When the ice went out in late spring they built a cradle for her and dragged her ashore. Their busy hands scraped her old paint down to the wood surface and, when she again floated gracefully on the water, the dazzling white and green of her hull and deckhouse brought exclamations of admiration from Jim's friends and of pride from Jim. "Shucks, there ain't no better work boat on the lakes—ain't she a honey!"

The war over, there was no immediate work for the *Islander*. Late in May, Jim heard from Ben. He had sold the store and was coming to Deep Harbor in early June. "If I can find the damn place," he added to his brief letter.

Jim carried the letter with him during the ensuing weeks and before long everyone knew that Jim's army pal was to pay him a visit. Many plans for his entertainment were volunteered, but Jim's reaction was always "Aw shucks, he just wants to go boat ridin' and fishin' and do lots of restin'."

Nevertheless the evening of Ben's arrival called for festivity. Jim took him from bar to bar and introduced him to all his friends. The townsfolk heard all about their escapades in Europe and the war in general and they responded to the gaiety and fun of the occasion by forgetting any distinction between the two wars in their spirited and spirit laden celebration. Reunions of war veterans often result in prolonged festivities that relevate the business at hand to secondary consideration, and so it was to be several days before Jim and Ben embarked upon a voyage aboard the *Islander*. When they did at last cast loose the mooring lines of the trim and shipshape craft, it was a warm June morning offering all the things that Jim had so boastfully promised— islands, fishing, and great water spaces.

Jim exhibited the prowess of his craft with pride. Dodging the great ore freighters, riding the crests of their foamy wakes, he fascinated Ben with his reckless daring and skillful maneuvering. A smart coast guard cutter passed to their port and Jim stepped out of the pilot house to doff his visored sailor's cap in comradely salutation. "Them's the policemen of the water," he explained.

"Do they ever bother you?" asked Ben.

"Aw shucks no. This boat's got documents and I got a pilot's license, see?" He emphasized his meaning by proudly pointing to the frames on the pilot house wall.

A week later while returning from a pleasure trip out on the big lake *below*, they noticed the late afternoon sun give way to lowering skies. The restless sea churned itself into increasing turbulence as the breakers dashed into glistening white foam against the rocky shore approaches. The *Islander* rode the sea with easy grace, her bow cutting through the heavy roll, her stern settling level and true as the crest passed amidships. As the little craft was rounding the rocky promontory a few miles below Deep Harbor where she would enter the oily smoothness of sheltered water, an ominous thud below deck was followed by the quiet of a stalled engine. Without speed or power to mind her helm, the *Islander* lurched in the trough of the ever increasing sea and passed helplessly from crest to crest toward the treacherous, rocky beach.

A few moments later she crashed, and with a sickening lurch her stern settled while the sea twisted her without mercy in a rocky embrace. Her aged planks, unable to withstand the tortuous strain, burst from her keel and frame and the water lashed through her open hull. Her bow settled on hard bottom in shallow water only a few rods from the shore, to which Jim and Ben waded quickly. Upon reaching land and safety, they turned to watch her break up. Her trim gunwales snapped and the pilot house was lapped by the rising water in the sinking stern. Almost reverently, Ben asked, "Whatcha gonna do now, Jim?"

"Aw shucks," replied Jim cheerfully, "ain't nothin' to buildin' a boat. I know where there's a good oak log that'll make a good keel and I'll git planks and it'll be no time at all before I'll have me a better boat than this one."

Then, without a word, he waded out into the surging and foam laden water. Deftly he seized her bow stem and lifted himself to her heaving, slanting deck. Scrambling on his knees to the pilot house, he emerged a moment later and leaped shoreward. Clutched tightly in his hand he held the precious document, and under his arm his framed pilot's license.

WINTER VIGIL

STEVE PALMER stirred himself to wakefulness. The deep gloom within the crudely furnished cabin and the snow specked windowpane attested to the coming of another night. Wearily he rose from the discomfort of the cushionless home built armchair and tossed another chunk of firewood into the long drum-like heating stove. For a moment he listened to the shrieking wind and the beating of its fury against the walls and windows and the single door. Shivering he lit the kerosene lamp. Its faint illumination served only to remind him of the stern reality of the personal crisis that wind and snow and bitter cold and the isolation of Big Island had compounded.

He walked to the bedside of his wife at the far end of the one room cabin; her labored breathing and the excessive warmth of her forehead offered no encouragement. On cots beside her lay their oldest child of four and another hardly two. Carefully and tenderly he placed cold wet cloths upon their feverish brows and listened with apprehension and helplessness to their whimpering moans. He bent fearfully over the improvised crib at the foot of his wife's bed. The tiny tot of three weeks was breathing heavily and irregularly.

For two days and nights his had been a ceaseless vigil, a vigil of hope and prayer and helplessness. And now it was to be another night like the one before and the one before that. It was to be another night of self-incrimination, of rage, of terror, of weariness, of fighting to stay awake, and of the crying of his tortured mind and body for the blessed respite of sleep. It was to be another night of listening to the shrieking tempest without, of hearing the hard driven snow beat against the windowpanes, of seeing its powdery whiteness sift through the cracks between the logs of the hut that was his home. It was to be another night when again and again the thundering reverberation of the invincible blizzard would reach a shuttering crescendo and spend itself in a diabolical moan against the towering pine and spruce surrounding the lonely cabin. Wearily Steve slumped into the chair in front of the stove and buried his face in his work gnarled hands.

The flickering light of the lamp cast crazy dancing patterns on the roughhewn logs of the cabin walls. From under the door the powdery snow was creeping into the center of the room. The relentless wind rattled the windows and the sheet iron chimney pipe drummed a metallic staccato in ominous refrain. On the rafters the frost glistened in long triangular patterns to end in wet dark spots where the heat of the roaring stove had melted it. There was nothing he could do but keep the fire going and think.

Of thinking he had done much these past few days and

nights, wearily and bitterly and despondently. His were troubled thoughts, thoughts that stirred in him a consciousness of personal guilt and responsibility for the defenseless circumstances into which he had led his cherished family, thoughts that sought vigorously to defend his chosen life and to approve the wisdom of his judgment. There were thoughts that sought desperately for a solution of the crisis confronting him, thoughts that probed into impossible realms of fantasy and miracle. And while he wearily watched the dull red glow climb high on the chimney of the burning stove and heard the fire roaring in unison with the hurricane, and while the thud of broken branches against the walls and roof told of the unabated fury of the storm, there came thoughts that reeled the panorama of his life before him and stilled the rage against his helplessness and impotence. They were pleasant thoughts of his childhood, of the cherished freedom of the great outdoors, and they numbed his misery and pain and brought peace and rest and—resignation.

The island was Steve's birthplace. As a toddling child he had followed his father through the woodlands and over the exciting trails and waterways, trapping, hunting, fishing, drawing the sap from maple trees. His had been a life of poverty, a poverty in which there was dignity and joy, in which the material requisites and complexities of modern living ended with the procurement of shelter, warmth, and food. In the flickering shadows of the lamp and the menacing howl of the wind there was woven the sight and sound of his childhood wandering, of beaver ponds, deer trails, and the dens of black bear. There was the sound of running water, the exciting tug of a fighting fish, the splash of a plummeting eagle upon its unsuspecting prey. There was the primitive and uncertain schooling, the delights of forest trails and the coziness and comfort of the deep, silent winters.

Seasons came and went and the freedom of their coming and going was matched by the freedom of life in the great wooded areas of Big Island, of life that began in the first faint murmuring of springtime when the pike and rainbows sought the snow water streams, when the mushrooms beckoned invitingly in the open glades, and summer crept into berry time and the deer displayed red coated arrogance in the green and purple shading of the bush.

And the fall would come and with it the preparations for winter that meant food and warmth and shelter. And when the snows glistened on the frozen lakes and bays and on the balsam and spruce, there came the delights of winter ease, relieved by the excitement of the trail, the pursuit of the snowshoe rabbit, and the elusive coyote, and occasionally of the wolf. There was time for fun and frolic and for boyish episodes.

In these carefree and happy circumstances he had grown to manhood, a manhood enriched by woodland lore and self-sufficiency. His manhood thoughts turned early to a cabin of his own, of a family and of children whose heritage would be a love of freedom and of space.

There came the war. With it came the boredom of army barracks, the confinement of troop transports, and the thrill of strange places. There came the hardships and perils of foxholes and beaches and always there was the thrill of looking forward to the day of his return.

Then within the comforting friendliness of the forests of Big Island he would build for himself and his childhood sweetheart a cabin. It would have a woodshed and a root cellar, and behind it would be a garden and before it a stream. There would be paths leading into distant thickets where the bears fought over wild berry patches—there would be runways where the deer would pass from the hardwoods to the stream edge—there would be beaver dams, and partridge bowers—there would be comfort, security, love—and there would be children.

And when that long awaited return finally came, he lost no time in gaining the fulfillment of his golden dreams. Long before he had shaken from his consciousness the restricting discipline of military life, he had cleared his cabin site, had cut and hewn his logs and had commenced his building. There were showers for his bride to be and bachelor parties for him. There was the wedding and that first blissful year and the children came and there was peace and quiet and cheer and always something to do that added to comfort, to security, and to happiness.

The woodshed was there and it was full of wood. The root cellar was there and it was full of vegetables. The lean-to was finished and it was stocked with game and provisions. And within the sturdy walls there was happiness and laughter and a new baby and winter was here.

It had been an open winter. But Steve was not to be deceived by a mild January and February. March could be bitter and cold and the snow could lie deeply and communications with distant neighbors or with the mainland could not be assured. He well knew the hardships and cruelty that capricious nature could impose upon the desolation and dangers of a winter bound and ice locked island habitude. And so with fierceness and determination he had prepared to forge around the happiness and security of his family a ring of assurance against want and the privation of isolation.

And so from distant mail order houses came blankets, trinkets, clothing, and a host of other supplies. He had planned well and amply for human need, including the delight and contentment that would shorten the confinement imposed by the long winter months.

And then came March and on its heels a belated winter that sought with its ferocity to atone for its late arrival. The snow lay heavy and deep in the forests and giant drifts covered the trails and roadways and the ice bridge, thick and snow covered over the straits to the mainland, heaved into cunningly concealed windrows and tortuous fissures.

There was treachery underfoot and there was treachery above. Returning home one mid-afternoon from his trap line, Steve found treachery also within the sanctity of his little family circle. In the few hours of his absence, an insidious malady had invaded the realm of his cherished hearthside to strike down his loved ones. And the March winds had begun the fiercest blow of the winter.

On snowshoes he had struggled through the rapidly deepening drifts to a local midwife. There he had breathlessly described the apparent symptoms. She could but instruct him in the administering of home medication and warn him of the need for medical skill and miracle drugs.

It was ten miles to Island Bay and then ten miles more over the treacherous ice bridge to the mainland. It was then sixty miles more to the nearest physician. In between lay the treachery of windrowed ice and miles of travel possible only on snowshoes, if one could succeed in withstanding the biting slash of bitter wind and the sting of flying snow particles. Then there were miles of snow blocked highways. Miracle drugs were needed, but it would take a miracle to obtain them.

Fiercely determined to spare no effort, Steve had fought his way through the towering drifts and the dense forests to Island Bay. With resolve and courage he had

struck out over the swirling white of the ice bridge, only to
find defeat in the treacherous arch of a precipitous windrow
and an ice crack from which the cold open water signalled
a cruel defiance.

Dejectedly he had fought his way back to his fever
stricken family to take up these days and nights of ceaseless,
agonizing vigil and tortuous soul searching. Was this the
price of the freedom of forests, rivers, lakes and streams,
and open sky?

.   .   .

He woke with a start. Bright sunlight streamed through
the windows and outside it was quiet. A perceptible chill
drew his attention to the fire and he paused to add fuel and
stir the dying embers. He peered briefly through the window and saw that the storm was over. Fearfully he strode to
his wife's bedside. Her smile told him that the fever had
broken. From the cots beside her came morning greetings
and childish demands for food.

He bent over the tiny crib; then, startled, he turned to
his wife. With no trace of sorrow or accusation, she mur-
mured, "Yes, I know."

Without a word, Steve prepared breakfast and attended to the household duties.

The noon sun was high in the heavens and the dazzling
white of snow laden pines glistened like myriads of precious
gems to form a fairyland of peace and purity and hope.
Steve's snowshoes crunched swiftly across giant drifts as he
strode with purpose and resolve. On his sturdy shoulders
he carried a tiny box of new pine wood. It was ten miles to
the settlement and he needed to return quickly to attend to
the chores and to wait upon his little family in the cabin
nestled in the forest near the stream.

INDIAN PETE

INDIAN PETE was a product of Big Island. As a boy he attended the settlement school where his playmates, both red and white, knew him as Dave Benny. His father and mother were a pair of shiftless Indians, since departed to other islands or perhaps to happier hunting grounds.

In his youth, Dave stayed within the family circle, contributing to the larder by weaving baskets, picking berries, or performing roustabout duties in the lumber camps. Aside from that, he lived precariously in abandoned shacks or, at times, in birch bark hovels. His father, a ward of a benign government, drank up most of the proceeds and frequently found protracted absences from the island necessary for his personal health and welfare. Despite this nomadic existence, Dave managed to get through eight grades in the settlement school and was accepted among the white boys as well as other Indian lads as a "good guy" and of equal social quality. This acceptance was, in fact, one of the admirable qualities of the island folks.

The eighth grade class of which Dave was a member gave a graduation play. It was a lurid western drama with pistol packing and murderous episodes involving a ferocious as well as illusive character known as Indian Pete. Dave, being qualified racially and temperamentally, and having a quality of mischievous mimicry, was chosen for the part, a choice in which no one was disappointed. The result was that the class made enough money to have a picnic and Dave won for himself a new name, that of Indian Pete. It was not that he was called so habitually in the subsequent years, since Islanders indulged in nicknames only for brevity or in fun. But "Indian Pete" became his name when conditions deemed it appropriate or convenient.

As Dave grew older, he gave every indication of following in his father's footsteps, except that he carried his shiftless heritage with decency and in good grace, and with an admirable quality of humor. The Islanders liked him, and on long winter nights his skill at mimicry and pantomime contributed much to the hilarity of their gatherings. His social acceptance and likeable qualities also assured him of enough odd job employment to provide for his meager needs. As Dave Benny, he was a good guy and commanded trust and respect. As Indian Pete, he was a fraud and deceived neither himself nor his island friends. But these friends, one and all, would be the last to expose his fraudulence.

It all came about like this. From the great industrial areas *below* the annual urge to don red coats and wield fire-arms in the exciting fifteen day chase of antlered deer drove great armies of would-be huntsmen into the vastness of the great country *above below*. They swarmed northward by train and bus and in vehicles of every description, converging upon the natural water barriers to tax all available facilities. Once past this barrier they sped north, east, and west, to be absorbed in great and uncrowded space, always seeking remoteness and isolation.

A trickle of the many sought the wild and pathless desolation of Big Island, to pursue there in its deep dark forest fastness elusive trophies for later boasting and display. The annual event became an important item in the primitive economy of Big Island, and crude facilities were rapidly improved to accommodate the pleasure bent visitors with their ready cash and boisterous intentions. They sought guides and food and beds and whisky, and the Islanders exerted every effort not to disappoint them.

They came from lathes and punch presses, from offices and stores, from city halls and banks and from brokerage houses. The Islanders eyed them speculatively and stretched their limited facilities for them. The tiny island ferry ran the clock around to carry their vehicles from the mainland, and the Islanders tucked them in spare rooms, barns, cabins, and in tents. The Hunters' Bar dressed up its frontier quality and stocked well in advance to administer to parched throats and to provide fun and frolic. For fifteen days each year the island belonged to the red coated visitors, and the welcome sign was the mystery of its towering pine and spruce and white birch shore line.

On one of these annual pilgrimages a sleek pretentious

limousine pulled to a stop on the approach ramp of the island ferry on the mainland, its occupants obviously impatient. The deck hand grinned at the ferry pilot and dutifully lowered the gate and beckoned the driver of the car on.

The back seat of the limousine was piled with luggage and gun cases of exquisite quality. In the front seat sat a large, florid faced man whose red plaid huntsman's garments concealed neither their newness nor their wearer's opulence and importance. Behind the wheel sat a slight, subservient appearing man, comical in his similar bright hued regalia, and apparently ill at ease. He was evidently a handy man serving in the dual capacity of chauffeur.

The florid gentleman stepped out of the car once it had been properly chocked on the deck of the ferry. After glancing apprehensively at the whitecaps and swells of the narrow strait, he engaged Corky, the deck hand, in conversation. They spoke first about island accommodations and then about the availability of guides. The deck hand was given to understand that by guide was meant not a part time participant in this intriguing profession but instead a first class woodsman of tried and true quality and professional rating. This sort of interrogation appealed to Corky's prankish nature.

Now Corky, a veteran of many annual migrations and a deckside spectator of the colorful parades, could accomplish more conversation in the brief ten minute crossing than a war correspondent could pack into half an hour of radio time. On this particular crossing he outdid himself in expressing his opinion of guides in general and in extolling the qualifications, virtues, and popularity of one in particular. Waiting until the craft had nearly reached the island landing and sensing that he had impressed the florid gentleman with his seriousness and authoritativeness, he bent closely and in lowered tones said, "Go to the Hunters' Bar and ask for Indian Pete."

And so that evening the florid gentleman elbowed his way through the crowds lined up at the rail and inquired of the bartender the whereabouts of Indian Pete. Hearing Dave called by his nickname for the first time in a decade, the bartender looked startled and the conversation at the rail quieted as the Islanders sensed the implication.

The bartender looked carefully over the crowd and then, busying himself by wiping glasses, he replied unhurriedly that Indian Pete usually came out of the woods at about eight in the evening. As it was only six at the time, he suggested that the gentleman return about then. He pointed to a knife scarred table and explained that that was where Indian Pete usually spent the evening. Then as an afterthought and in all seriousness, the bartender added that he was sorry that he could not direct the gentleman to where Indian Pete lived, since no one on the island knew other than that it was somewhere in the deep woods south of the crossroads and that he moved his abode often.

As a matter of fact, Indian Pete was at that very moment sleeping on an old mattress topping several tiers of beer cases just the thickness of the wall away from the bar room. When the gentleman departed with his faithful handy man close at his heels, the bartender and the Islanders exchanged knowing glances and shortly thereafter they closeted themselves with Dave.

Dave, having been rudely awakened from a deep sleep intended to condition him for an evening of bar room frolic, rubbed his eyes in disbelief and protest. He had never shot a deer in his life and didn't know where to look for them and, as for bear, he wouldn't stay within a mile of one if he

knew about it. And as far as trackless forests were concerned, the only walking he cared to do was across a bar
room floor or while thumbing a ride on a gravelled road.
And to all this he added his noble Redman's heritage notwithstanding.

But the prospect of a hundred dollar fee and some fun
on the side finally won Dave over and the stage was set. He
was to make his appearance half an hour late in order to
properly impress his client.

Promptly at eight the important personage came into
the bar room flanked by his subservient escort. Other hunters gave him a brief glance, but the Islanders paid him no
heed as he sought a seat from which he could watch the
scarred top table. Oddly enough, though the place was
crowded, Pete's table remained empty.

The florid gentleman drummed his fingers impatiently
and from time to time glanced at his watch and then let his
eyes rove to the several doors leading from the outside. His
irritation was in no way eased by bottles of beer which had
had but brief association with refrigeration.

Occasionally the crowds moved to and fro and obscured for the moment his point of observation. Time
moved on and with it irritability mounted.

A fist fight at the opposite end of the room drew everyone's attention and particularly distracted the waiting pair.
But it ended in what was perhaps a mock belligerency. The
florid gentleman returned to his watch over the empty table
and nearly lost his aplomb to see a brooding Redman sitting
quietly and impassively in the deep gloom of the dimly lit
bar room, staring straight ahead.

Upon his head he had a fur cap, underneath which
there showed a narrow red silk band. Wisps of crow black
hair gleamed over his shiny bronze forehead, and his high

cheek bones cast shadows over his lower face. He wore a
purple shirt with a bright yellow kerchief, and a brown
buckskin jacket with long fringes. In his belt of bright hand
tooled leather there was a sheathed knife of villainous proportions. He wore blue jeans whose bottoms were tucked in
the upper flair of moccasin boots. His hands lay one above
the other and, protruding from beneath the purple sleeve,
a bronzed wrist carried a heavy silver bracelet.

For a moment Florid Face was frozen into immobility.
Then, slowly and almost reverently, he approached Pete's
table. There he coughed several times but disturbed not at
all the imperturbability of Indian Pete. Seating himself, and
with several false and ineffective starts, he finally succeeded
in extracting a deep, guttural "How," and it was as though
it expressed the dignity, courage, and sorrow of a savage
lineage going back to the coming of the first white man.

There ensued a series of spoken words and frantic gesticulations, punctuated by grunts, with Indian Pete playing
his role of hard to get in a manner that would have won acclaim even from the most discriminating audience. It ended
with Florid Face placing on the table a twenty dollar bill,
whereupon Pete rose and with masterful dignity traced
slowly upon the table five careful strokes and then pointed
to the bill. Florid Face nodded in quick agreement, Pete
grunted "Meetum sun up," and with dignity befitting a
high chieftain he turned abruptly and vanished as suddenly
as he had come.

In the backroom he and his co-conspirators laughed
loudly. Pete yanked off his regalia and chuckled at the
bosomy expanse of the borrowed buckskin jacket. Then,
after washing the grease from his face, he settled down to a
bottle of beer and contemplation of his entry into an unfamiliar profession. He listened attentively to the earnest di-

rections and advice of his friends. When he was certain that Florid Face and his companion had departed, he joined the crowd in the bar room. Of one thing he could be certain— his island friends would leave no stone unturned to assist him in this masquerade.

.　　　.　　　.

Early the next morning the sleek limousine halted in a stand of hardwood on a deep rutted roadway. Pete's friends had told him that there was nothing to this guide business and that he had only to find a patch of hardwood along some back road and sit on a log and wait for some animal to expose itself. Pete fervently hoped that the log would not be too far away and that the animal would not be a bear.

Pete alighted from the automobile and assumed all of the characteristics of a professional guide plus some of the Redman's tactics which he had read about in the comics. Touching his lips lightly to caution silence and bending low and moving noiselessly, he led Florid Face through the thicket in the best tradition of storybook stalking. Certainly the amusing picture of a buckskin clad Redman followed by a roly poly wad of scarlet wool did not fit into any ancestral pattern that he might have learned from his forefathers. Pete was much relieved to find a log before his muscles, unaccustomed to such needless exercise, signalled any serious protest.

Florid Face expressed surprise that Pete carried no rifle to which Pete, comfortably seated upon the log, replied in sign language that he scorned such modern appurtenances in favor of his sheath knife and then in unmistakably haughty disgust with Florid Face's loquacity he cautioned him by signs to keep his mouth shut lest he frighten every living thing into hiding.

Florid Face had hardly had time to digest this admonition when as noble a buck as ever graced a mantelpiece stepped out from a stand of small cedars close by and presented a broadside target so vulnerable that even the extreme case of buck fever that at once possessed Florid Face could hardly deflect his aim enough to miss. The expensive rifle spoke just once and the fine animal jumped straight into the air, then dropped into a quivering heap, and lay still. Florid Face was too surprised and excited to note the consternation on the otherwise impassiveness of Pete's countenance. Without having had any previous experience in slashing a buck's throat and disemboweling him, Pete did a credible job of this first requisite of a professional guide, much as it may have been distasteful to him.

Early that afternoon, Corky blinked in amazed incredulity as a big limousine with a twelve point buck rolled majestically onto the island ferry headed for the mainland and a florid faced gentleman of obvious means and importance slipped a ten dollar bill into his palm and whispered, "Thanks for the tip, Buddy."

Back of the counter of the Hunters' Bar, Dave Benny pounded his ears in deep and audible slumber on his beer case supported mattress and dreamed of the purchase possibilities of five crisp twenty dollar bills.

Little did Dave know that the startlingly successful hoax compounded by his cronies and by the prankish deck hand of the island ferry was the beginning of fame and fortune and of a masquerade which was to tax his cunning and duplicity for years to come.

Down *below*, over cocktails, fragrant Havanas, and sumptuous luncheon tables in the lush, deep carpeted club rooms of the elite, Florid Face boasted of his big game prowess and his privileged association with a superb survivor of the vanishing Redman in the hinterlands of the great north wilderness. Supported by snapshots and wild exaggeration, he extolled the virtues, skill, and cunning of Indian Pete, and the story of the twelve point buck was told and retold, reaching even the columns of local news commentators. Would-be Nimrods nurtured deep seated longings for the excitement, danger, and adventure of moving silently through dark and pathless forests with a noble Redman as their companion. They little dreamed that at that moment Indian Pete was picking up loose change as a baby sitter while folks of the now back to normal Big Island were meeting at the school house to plan for Christmas programs and celebrations. And the fact that his job included the washing of the family dishes hardly contributed to Pete's personal feeling of nobility.

Pete might have spent his idle time between hunting seasons in belatedly learning something about the lore of the woods and the habits of hunted animals. But this required a great deal of exertion, and he reasoned furthermore that there was no point in bothering with this when showmanship served as an acceptable substitute. In subsequent years he allowed his hair to grow long just before the hunting season. He affected a mock temperament and required a rigid standard of deportment on the part of his clients. When an expedition under his guidance hinted of failure, and most of them did, he would contrive to become displeased with the conduct of his party and would stalk away in high disdain and with haughty air, leaving them to fend for themselves. Having collected his fee in advance, this in no way affected his profit, and Pete reasoned wisely that there were more suckers where these came from.

In company with his cronies, Pete enlisted the advantages of salt blocks, rutabagas, and potatoes in attracting his antlered prey, and engaged also in night shining. A co-operative arrangement was thereby compounded which included the sale of preslaughtered carcasses to certain of the whisky-drinking, card-playing red coats. While he outwardly viewed such transactions with noble distaste, Pete inwardly delighted in the ease of the attendant profit.

In later years, he cunningly demanded increased fees, running into a considerable sum to be doubled if his guidance resulted in success, and successes were usually contrived with the help of a co-conspirator. For this purpose, Pete usually led a fruitless chase which ended late in the afternoon in a long shot which even an expert marksman would deem a waste of ammunition. When the distant animal high-tailed into the thicket he would shout a reassuring "Gottem!" and then would begin a trailing exhibition that aroused wonder and admiration. When darkness fell, Pete would take out his sheath knife and blaze a tree as a marker. Then he would grunt an optimistic "Find 'em sun up."

Surprisingly enough, the morning resumption of trailing usually led to a successful conclusion within a few hundred yards. And of course the overnight interval was a satisfactory explanation of the rigor mortis that was evident in the carcass. As far as the flavor of the meat was concerned, Pete preferred hamburgers anyway.

Pete's natural ability for acting and his exceptional success in capitalizing on his racial background provided for him a life of ease. During the brisk fifteen days of the open season he earned all the cash needed to sustain him for the remaining three hundred and fifty. That meant for Pete lazy summer days of lolling in the sun's pleasant warmth and evenings of gossiping at the settlement store or of playing rummy at the Bar. Pete was as natural to, and as much a part of, the island as were the tall, white birch and the deep, green spruce trees that drew the ever increasing urban visitors. Above all, the islanders liked Pete, not only for himself, but perhaps for the color and glamour that his tall slim form and swarthy countenance added to the already prodigious charm of their island.

Well meaning friends tried to persuade Pete to also cash in on the summer groups seeking the flavor of wilderness life and enchantment. But Pete stoutly resisted, shuddering at the very thought of such waste of energy and time that might better be spent in pleasant daydreaming or in the comradeship of playing cards and drinking beer. Besides, he was afraid of boats and was sure that some damn fool tourist would want to take his picture in a canoe simulating the brave feats and skills of his noble forefathers. He had seen just such things in moving pictures, and wanted no part of these glamorous, Hiawatha roles. He preferred instead to look the part while keeping his feet firmly on the ground.

There came a hunting season that broke all records in the swarms that overran Big Island. Deer were plentiful and it took no particular skill, and much less an Indian guide, to bag a buck. Pete, as usual, was cashing in.

It was close to the last day and the army had been thinned out considerably. The evenings at the Bar were spent in long sessions of boastful talk in which the relative merits of Winchester Specials, 30-30's, 32's, and other formidable weapons loomed important. Here and there was a stout defender of a hard hitting though comparatively inaccurate rifle, supported by the claim that most deer were bagged only a few hundred feet distant. As often as not, the high-velocity flat-trajectory boys would leap into the fray, vowing that to be a successful Nimrod on Big Island one had to be able to send a superbly accurate lethal bullet a distance of no less than a thousand yards or go back empty handed. To this the short-shot hard-hitting enthusiasts would inquire how in hell a buck could be distinguished from a doe at that distance, only to find themselves at the end of a limb when the opposition cited examples of hunters, particularly ones under the guidance of one Indian Pete, whose successes were at spectacularly great distances.

Through all of this Pete would sit at the scarred top table in apparent oblivion to his surroundings, his eyes fixed, his face immobile, as if he were looking down the ageless vista of his great ancestry, roaming forests teeming with wild game and most certainly void of any pale faced, red clad tenderfeet. More likely he was dreaming of the hours remaining before he could discard the ridiculous paraphernalia of his noble warrior masquerade and junk his female buckskin fringes, red band, and yellow kerchief to don his infinitely more comfortable blue jeans and flannel shirt and sit in on a game of rummy.

In the crowd around the bar were two men who, while not entering into the arguments, took an intense interest in the educational value of the firearm discussions. They had been around most of the season and were apparently a pair of luckless Nimrods. At least they wore the red trousers and jackets and carried the usual sheath knives in their belts. The bar room crowd had seen enough of them during the past ten days to label them appropriately "Specs" and "Professor." These appellations had reference to the fact that one wore glasses and the other had a scholarly appearance, and both had about them an air of respectable reticence and formality.

When these two later engaged Pete in what was apparently a bargaining conversation, the barkeeper and the few remaining Islanders exchanged knowing winks. Pete had another pair of suckers on the hook. The conversation was accompanied by grunts and gesticulations and ended as usual with Pete scribing his figure with his forefinger, the eager bargainers nodding assent, and a terse "Meetum high sun," followed by Pete's wraith-like fade out.

Promptly at noon the next day Specs and Professor picked up Indian Pete at the Bar. Pete noted with disdain the rather nondescript car they drove. Association with a more pompous and wealthy clientele had made him rather callous in his mercenary pursuits.

In the course of the afternoon's tramping and log sitting it occurred to Pete that he had yet to steer a dumber pair in search of big game. But he acted his part throughout, a bronzed and skillful hunter and a glamorous specimen of a noble, vanishing race.

It was late afternoon when Pete settled them on a comfortable ground balsam carpet behind a huge log. The blind commanded a view of a long narrow open area at the far end of which a thinly timbered glade fronted the dense cedar swamp behind it. Pete sat like a statue, frowning whenever his companions moved about or spoke. He was probably weighing the advantages of finding some fault with their deportment which would give him an opportunity to terminate the expedition in a fit of haughty temperament. On the other hand, this was the last day of the season and maybe the double fee might come in handy. It was yet an hour before sundown, and Pete knew that the distant glade was a rendezvous for a couple of unattached does. This much at least he had learned in his years as a professional guide. Perhaps it might be best to wait it out for another half an hour.

Pete saw them first, but waited for his companions to spot them. Two does, their dark brown coats gleaming in the sunlight, were slowly working their way out into the open. Soon Specs gesticulated excitedly and drew Professor's attention to them. At a thousand yards it was, of course, impossible to see if they carried antlers.

Both men looked questionably at Pete, who pointed to the one on the right and grunted "Him buck."

Pete watched them set their sight elevations for the distance and take careful aim, while he inwardly felt contempt for their childish faith in the keenness of his eyesight and their dumb optimism in expecting to hit something at that distance. Their guns spoke as one and both animals showed their white flags as they leaped toward the cedar thicket. "Gottem," said Pete, in a tone that implied admiration for such marksmanship, and the three hurried to the glade to track the wounded animal.

For half an hour Specs and Professor followed Pete as he traced a line of invisible tracks or paused momentarily to read the strategy of the fleeing animal; all of this was done in a manner that would have amazed even his scalp lifting forebears. As for the two gullible Nimrods, they could only marvel at a keenness of vision that could read tracks and signs which were invisible to them even when Pete pointed them out. At one place, he stopped abruptly, studied the ground carefully, and announced, "Him bad hit—lay down here rest and go again."

Then, casting a speculative glance sunward, Pete slashed a tree and continued, "Pretty soon him lay down and die—too dark to see soon—we come back sunup and find him."

Specs and Professor were agreeably surprised to find the rutted roadway so close at hand as Pete led them from the thicket.

That evening on his mattress bower in the storage room behind the bar, Pete listened to the persuasive arguments of Dip Crawford. Dip was all for shining a buck that evening, as they had often done before, and planting the carcass near the slashed tree in the cedar thicket. Pete could then lead Specs and Professor to a successful finish in their trailing of the wounded deer. "Hell, Dave," Dip argued, "it's a hundred dollars for one buck split between you and me and besides it's the last chance of the season."

Pete was convinced.

As they walked through the bar room, Pete noticed that Specs and Professor had already left. Feeling a bit that way himself, he smiled inwardly at their probable fatigue from the afternoon chase, and envied their early retirement.

Dip's pickup truck stood in readiness outside. In half an hour they stopped on a rutted road near Shelter Cove. From under a canvas and a mass of balsam boughs in the rear of the truck Dip pulled a rifle and a flashlight and handed the latter to Pete.

They settled themselves under a spacious spruce bower facing the waters of the cove. The moon cast shimmering light upon the quiet surface. They had not long to wait. A doe strolled along the waters' edge, turning a cautious head from side to side, her huge ears a striking pattern of alertness. Unhurriedly she continued on her way, pausing to turn her head to the rear. Dip nudged Pete. That meant a buck was following, he whispered.

With slowness, exasperating slowness, a huge buck moved into their line of vision. His large rack was plainly silhouetted on the dull ivory of the background waters. Carefully Dip raised his rifle and waited for the buck to turn his head in their direction. At just the right moment Pete sent a stab of light into the darkness that brought two gleaming gems sharply into focus. The buck crashed to the ground, the echo of Dip's rifle died away, and all was silence.

They remained in their concealment long enough to feel assured that the telltale report of the rifle had not drawn inquisitive visitors. Then, dragging the carcass to the truck, they swung it atop the canvas and deftly hid it with the balsam boughs. It was only a few miles to the crooked lumber trail near the open glade, and they traveled in discomfort and uncertainty, without turning on their headlights. Arriving at the point in the road nearest to Pete's slashed tree, they stopped and prepared to unload the carcass for planting.

A pair of dazzling headlights from a parked and partially concealed car suddenly bathed them with revealing light. They stared in utter amazement as the figure of Professor approached them, carrying a rifle in his hand. The canvas of Dip's pickup rustled, and from under it Specs appeared and ordered them to face the car lights.

Reaching into the truck, Specs extracted the cartridges from their rifle and tossed them in the bush. Then, in a brisk and business-like voice he asked for their licenses. Dip had none. Neither had Pete. Coolly and with unconcealed mockery, Specs then cited them for their transgressions:

1. Hunting without a license.
2. Shining deer with artificial light.
3. Killing deer at night.
4. Possession of illegal venison.
5. Carrying loaded firearms in a vehicle.
6. Transporting illegal venison.
7. Shooting deer after the closing hour of the open season.

It was then and only then that Pete saw the frightening evidence of their authority, a gleaming badge which read,

"STATE CONSERVATION COMMISSION, SPE–
CIAL DEPUTY."

Crisply Specs ordered, "Crawford, you drive your
truck," and to Professor, "you ride with him."

Specs then turned to the crestfallen Pete and said, not
without amusement, "You, Hiawatha, hop in with me—
the judge wants to see you."

Pete did not answer to this with his usual guttural
grunt, but expressed instead the humiliation of a descending star with a polite, servile, "Yes sir."

.   .   .

The first evening after the closing day of the season is
always a dull one at the Hunters' Bar. The barkeeper was
hunched over a pair of chairs reading the comic section of a
week old paper. In the dim light of a corner booth, a four-
some of natives was playing a desultory game of rummy.
The only other occupant was a bearded, sleeping lumberjack, uncomfortably slouched over a scarred top table.

There was no joyous clinking of change, nor the customary rough talk and raucous laughter. On the bar as usual
was the slotted tin can with the sign,

GIVE TO THE CRIPPLED CHILDREN'S FUND

Next to it was a cooky jar. A square of paper pasted on it
read,

GIVE TO BAIL OUT DAVE BENNY
AND PAY HIS FINE

The island folks were that way.

CONSERVATION

CONSERVATION officer Chet Ollson was a nice guy. At least that is what the folks around Deep Harbor and the broad spaces of Big Island said about him. To say that about a game warden was a most charitable thing, considering their opinion of game wardens in general, which was not much in the backwoods of this land *above below*.

Young Ollson, fresh out of training school and only recently indoctrinated in the principles of conservation and law enforcement as related to protection of wild life, had accepted his badge of authority with eager resolve to perform this public service with honest endeavor. Unlike his many predecessors whose warden's services smacked of political appointment, he had won his spurs by serious educational preparation and arduous vocational training. Quite naturally Chet prosecuted the duties of his calling with a measure of youthful idealism—and ego. How was he to know that in this, his first area of wild life guardianship, the mortality rate of idealism and ego was frightfully high? The training manual did not say so.

In fact, Ollson was to learn that there were a lot of things the manual did not say. For example, there was that pamphlet that the commission published for the benefit of housewives. It told of ways in which to prepare more appetizing meals of venison and waterfowl, of beaver tail and gamy grouse, and of pike and bass and trout and perch. That the folk who dwelt within this land of such abundant wild life had culinary opinions of their own which were in conflict with such things as closed seasons was not mentioned. The pamphlet did not say that venison was at its best in August and September, whereas the legal open season was not until the blustery days of late November. It did not say that waterfowl on their protected northward migration in the spring were tastier and more tender than when they left the northern marshes to risk the legal barrage of gunfire on their flight to warmer climes. The good folk who dwelt within the forest bowers amid the islands and sparkling waters of the land *above* had secrets of their own that added zest and flavor to the fish and fowl and flesh that the abundance of the land afforded.

Neither did the manual mention that the warmth of Chet's acceptance among the folk was not necessarily an index of cooperative promise or of esteem, nor that salutation by his first name indicated endorsement of the authority of his calling. There were just a lot of things about which the manual neglected to inform him.

Time was within the memory of even those of middle age when the Indian population outnumbered the white, and the products of the forest, lake, and stream made possible a degree of self-sufficiency for both. Then came the gas buggy. It followed improved trails, which became roads and then highways, and with them came people from outside. Some came to stay and sink their roots in a soil of questionable livelihood, others to reap for the moment the bounty of the land and leave again to proclaim its merits.

Wild beasts and fowl and fish were killed as a matter of exhilarating sport instead of as a means of sustenance and they suffered from abuse of this privilege. Then came the laws that sought the preservation of this wilderness heritage from such thoughtless, wasteful extermination. The principle of conservation extended its arm of authority to stay unregulated slaughter and, hewing to the line, it cared not where the chips might fall. And they fell first upon the folk who deemed wild game for food their natural right, closed seasons or the manner of acquisition notwithstanding.

And so there was introduced into the independent and complacent atmosphere of the wooded spaces a new type of law enforcement. It affected livelihood and in consequence it was resisted. It sought to regulate the taking of that which the folk believed was theirs, and hence it outraged their independence. It was administered by men who flaunted badges but knew not the character of the people, nor the subtleness and cunning of their passive disobedience and contempt for law.

A generation was to pass before Chet Ollson's day. It was a generation in which the majesty of law enforcement and the recalcitrant dwellers of these forests clashed in senseless injustice and vindictive violations, creating humorous situations and violence too.

Game wardens do not like to be targets for playful pot shots. This was the folk's favorite form of intimidation;

harmless as the intent may have been, it resulted in short tenures of office and the frequent appearance of new appointees. The wardens' judgments varied as to methods of apprehension and they dissipated the good will they may have brought with them by injudicious arrests for petty infractions while major violators badgered them into ludicrous situations.

When kindly Father Dunnegan sought to bolster the finances of a struggling mission by the proceeds of a picnic that featured roast venison, his Godly intentions were in conflict with the laws of conservation, and the burly game warden bounced upon the festive crowd to confiscate the evidence. However much this may have been in conformity with the warden's sworn duty, it endeared him not one whit to the fiery priest nor his several hundred parishioners. The good Father invoked Biblical passages in support of his protestations, but in vain. The picnickers ate the pickles and the cake and listened glumly to his earnest exhortations. He attacked not at all the precept of the law, but he denounced its application with passionate vehemence. God created man in his own image and stocked the forests, lakes, and rivers to supply him food. Laws were not intended to deprive man of this bounty. Such laws pertained to wanton killing in the name of sport.

Having proclaimed a doctrine of this interpretation, the priest launched a tirade against the warden, stressing the despicable confiscation of the picnic venison. His thundering denunciation was interrupted by the arrival of a fresh supply and the parishioners hurried to prepare the kill in huge roasting pits.

When ailing, bedridden Grandma Kuski expressed a desire for a good old fashioned squirrel pie, grandson Charley set forth with a small caliber rifle to see that her wish was fulfilled. It would be another month before squirrel season opened, but by that time grandma might be beyond mortal appetite.

The youngster, heading for home with a brace of squirrels and a fat partridge that had inadvertently invited marksmanship, was seized by the game warden currently serving the area. The elder Kuski's expressions of outrage did not perturb the conscientious guardian of wild life, who served notice on the gentleman to appear before a distant justice of the peace on behalf of his wayward son. Meanwhile, he kept the rifle as security for appearance and—of course, the squirrels too. Whatever effect this may have had on grandma is inconsequential, but the effect upon the Polish population did in no wise add to the popularity of wild life protection in general, nor game wardens in particular.

The cook at Sabin's lumber camp was worried. Soapy, whose nickname stemmed from his propensity for strong soaps and plenty of suds, could see it coming. The score of lumberjacks who tucked their mud spattered boots under his table thrice each day were grumbling. Spring had started, and conditions in the woods with melting snows, combined with the impetuousness that comes from itchy palms and ready cash at the season's approaching end, were provocative of faultfinding and dissatisfaction. All through the long winter the hungry crews had devoured his flapjacks, roast beef, and potatoes in a manner that flattered his culinary prowess.

The first inkling of trouble came when the lumberjacks referred to Soapy's coffee as boiler compound and his flapjacks as boot soles. Such derogatory remarks earlier in the season would have been met by threatening gestures with a meat cleaver. But the logs lay in the woods, skidding snow was rapidly disappearing, and the bossman would forgive no provocation that might send the grumbling woodsmen townward and barward with their season's pay tucked in their money belts. The concoction of such appetizing offerings as potato dumplings, gingerbread, and chicken à la king in no wise allayed the ground swell of revolt.

Soapy lay in his bunk and pondered the vexing predicament. Mentally he reviewed his inventory. Spices, onions, carrots—why hadn't he thought of it before? Venison stew—that would perk them up.

It was still dark when the teams and bobsleds left camp the following morning. Unmindful of the stack of unwashed dishes, pots, and kettles, Soapy waited only until the last woodsmen had left the camp. Taking his rifle he walked quickly to the tamarack marsh nearby. He did not have to wait long. A yearling buck sauntered from a brush screen and stood quietly staring, followed by a sleek doe. Soapy chose the former, and a few moments later he was dragging the gutted carcass to the camp.

The men filed in that noon and silently took their places at the table. Platters heaped with fried sausage, fluffy mashed potatoes, natural gravy, and corn bread provoked no appreciative comments, nor did coffee and apple pie. If they noted the high spirits and secretive air with which Soapy dashed about to wait on them, it was not evident in their continued sullenness and silence. Never mind, thought Soapy, the stew at supper will fetch 'em.

No chef in any famous hostelry ever put forth greater effort to prepare so sumptuous an evening meal. And no group of gourmets ever ate with greater relish, nor in an atmosphere of such appetizing aroma and good will. And no cook ever experienced a more warming glow of pride than was Soapy's lot as the men pitched into the dessert course of mince pie surcharged with brandy, meanwhile quaffing

steaming mugs of coffee and extolling in the rough vocabulary of their calling the quality of his preparation.

Soapy was whistling happily 'mid the banging of pots
and kettles the following morning when an officious stranger entered the cook shack carrying a fresh deer hide. "Yep,
I shot it yesterday, and did dem boys go after dat stew," was
his reply to the stranger's curious inquiry.

It was twenty miles to the local justice of the peace in
the lumber town of Fairbanks where Soapy had his hearing, but the "boys," as he so affectionately called them,
went along to back him up. In the kitchen of a rough board
shack the law held forth. The warden stated his case. Soapy,
in simple innocence and unable to understand this extraordinary procedure, replied to the justice's question, "Sure I
kill it. Dem boys was hungry for stew and I gif it to 'em."

And while the boys milled around the doorway grumbling, the justice laboriously scrawled out the legal words of
the violation on an official form. His sympathy obviously on
the side of Soapy, he read the penalty prescribed and the
lumberjacks passed the hat to pay the fine. It was probably
not quite by accident that the warden a few days later
pulled up at conservation headquarters in Channel City mi-
nus his trousers and tendering his resignation.

Tony Chevalier steered his tiny fish tug gingerly past
the shoal waters off Juniper Island and cut his engine as he
approached the shallow bar off Shelter Cove. His net stakes
and floats showed plainly in the gleaming water ahead.
Reaching the first stake, he unloosened his crude derrick
boom fastened to the cedar spar. Working quickly, he began the harvest of his net set. At each lift he sorted out the
undersize and tossed them overboard. The bottom of his
boat was soon covered by the glistening silver of slimy,
wriggling fish.

Midway the length of his set he paused to light a cigarette and to rest from his labors. Here and there undersize fish were floating belly up, and Tony shook his head sadly at the waste. The law governed his net size and compelled him to return any fish that were less than legal length. Many would be dead or spent in their struggle to escape. Back in Deep Harbor the folks were hard put to feed hungry mouths in this year of job scarcity and low tourist income. They could use these wasted fish which even now the gulls were scooping up, diving amid screaming chatter and wild cries and fighting over choice morsels. "Tain't right," he muttered to himself and then, as if impelled by righteous indignation, he resumed his labors.

Expertly he culled each lift. Legal size were tossed aft to join the slimy mass. Those undersize ones that squirmed with healthy vigor, their scales unmarred, he slid back into the water. The dead and injured he flipped deftly under the cowling of the bow.

It was near sundown when he tied his tug to the spiles of the rotting dock structure in Deep Harbor. Into neat white pine boxes he packed the legal catch for market. Children from the nearby houses of the village gathered to watch him as he scraped and cleaned and packed. Dragging out some sodden newspapers, Tony divided the undersize fish into neat piles upon them. These he folded carefully and handed to each of the watching children, noting the pleased surprise on their little faces as they eagerly accepted the offering and scampered away to their homes.

Pleased with his charitable contributions, however small, to the good folks of Deep Harbor, Tony continued to bring in the undersize fish that did or could not survive his nets. The crowd of children expanded rapidly as word of the generous gesture spread through the village homes.

News also reached the ears of those whose duty it was to enforce the letter of the law. And so it was that on one evening strangers stood with the group of waiting children as Tony slid his little fish tug alongside the slippery spiles to unload his day's harvest.

Notwithstanding kindly intentions or the principle of feeding people instead of gulls, Tony paid the price. It would be many months before he would be able to purchase anew the confiscated nets, and they would be months of bewildering dismay and misunderstanding shared by the good people of the village—and the children.

These things were in the past when Chet saw for the first time this lovely wooded area. The good Father had long since gone to his reward, and so had Grandma Kuski. Most of the parishioners lived on and so also their children. The youthful Kuski had long since reached manhood's estate. Sabin's lumber camp lay in moldy, brushgrown decay, while Soapy perhaps had followed the westward trend of the declining logging industry. A few husky woodsmen had settled down to plots of ground to raise their food and to rear families that would long portray the character of the woodland folk. Tony no longer rippled the waters of Island Bay with his chugging little fish tug on the journeys to his nets, and the children who had once waited so eagerly his landing at the spiles now worried over children of their own and hoped for better days. Traditions are not written from pages of local history. They are wrought from resentments and from commendations relating to incidents long since forgotten in the misty past, but which persist in the moral vigor of customs and beliefs. And this Chet was soon to learn.

Through the land of Deep Harbor and Big Island a single gravel road winds in senseless deviation from purpose-

ful direction through the seemingly endless forest, linked
by a tiny ferry that carries the sparse traffic over the strait
to connect the mainland with the enchanting loneliness of
the wooded island. From this sequestered artery of travel a
few rutted roads and wagon trails slink through leafy bowers to end perhaps in charming coves and bays of distant
water fronts or to lose themselves in meaningless dispersion.
If, as it must be, these routes of travel serve purposes of
commerce and convenience, they touch but a tiny fraction
of the great spaces within which dwells the wild life whose
protection was the responsibility of Chet Ollson.

In a sturdy pickup he explored tirelessly the vast area,
to the end that its geography in terms of beaver dams and
deer yards, and the many other characteristics of this game
area, were as familiar to him as the simplicity and austerity
of the tiny room which was his lodging. The folk marveled
at his industry and from their admiration sprang the affectionate gesture of speaking to and of him by his nickname.
And while they learned to know Chet, Chet in turn learned
to know them—or so he thought.

His first arrest was prompted by an unknown informer.
As he was leaving his boardinghouse one noon he found a
scrawled note on his windshield stating the make of car, the
license number, and the location. That was all. Chet hastened and found a blustering tourist from *below* with a
string of fish caught out of season. This was but one of many
friendly tips which were to build for him an admirable record of enforcement and to bring favorable commendation
from his superiors.

Chet's youthful enthusiasm clouded his power of dis-
cernment, else he would have read in the friendliness and
cooperativeness a deception and stratagem prompted by tradition. He might have wondered why violators apprehended

by him were always from outside, rather than to have accepted the conclusion that, locally at least, game laws were observed with meticulous solicitude. He was yet to learn that the knobby treads with which his vehicle tires were equipped traced his comings and goings on the moist woodland roadways with unfailing veracity and that such information was quickly conveyed to those interested in his movements. He was to learn as he travelled back and forth between the mainland and the island that a cordial greeting from Corky on the ferry was meant less as a welcome sign than as informative recognition to be passed on to all who might have reason to be alert to a warden's visit.

Things might have stayed like this except that Spike Campbell shot a bear. It came about this way. When the winter's snow fell victim to the warmth of April showers, great hordes of silvery smelt rushed to lay their annual spawn in the many tiny streams that emptied into Island Bay. With nets and screen decked forks the natives shovelled great heaps of them into baskets, buckets, washtubs, and boxes. Spike, so named because of his snaggle-toothed countenance, was one of those whose greed exceeded his capacity to gut and scale them all, and after hours of this wearisome chore he decided to use the rest for fertilizer. It was much easier to spade up a few square yards of garden than it was to finger the slimy things, and so the fish were buried in the soft moist loam.

He never got around to planting a garden, and so the spaded patch gathered weeds and took on a distinctive odor. Spike happened to be away on some inconsequential errand when a large bear, attracted by the enticing odor—enticing, of course, in a bear sense only—came out of the bush to investigate. The garden patch was only a step or two from the cabin porch, and Mrs. Campbell chose this propitious moment to dump a dishpan of water over the porch rail.

It landed on the bear, and he let forth with a surprised grunt and rose majestically on his haunches. Mrs. Campbell uttered one whoop and fled inside. Thoroughly frightened, she screeched at the top of her voice in the vain hope that her cries of terror would somehow reach the nearest neighbor a mile away through dense impenetrable undergrowth.

To hear it told afterward, she screeched for several hours. At least, by the time Spike returned with his chugging, stripped-down jalopy, the audibility of her cries had been reduced to a wheezy sob, and the bear, unable to reconcile the combination of strange smells and sounds, was busy trying to gain entry into the cabin. He had already stripped down the screen cloth on the front windows and was busily engaged in a thorough demolition of the screen door when Spike rolled him over with a well placed bullet.

Chet heard about the incident the next day and proceeded to the scene to investigate. While it was closed season on bear, the state took a rather lenient attitude toward killing them out of season under the Campbell circumstances. On the other hand, Chet had to make out quite an involved report concerning predatory bears, particularly if they paid the death penalty for their marauding.

Chet arrived at the Campbell cabin about suppertime, a habit which he had learned early. The Campbells, still excited and upset, invited him to sit and he accepted with alacrity and pleasure. Knowing the Campbells to be folks of extremely limited means, he stared incredulously at the generously heaped platter of appetizing meat patties which had the appearance of expensive country sausage. Chet had had several outsize helpings before he realized that this was ground venison, well flavored with spice and onion, a dish that would arouse enthusiasm in the breast of the most accomplished gourmet. This being August, the venison was, however, most certainly out of season. Chet pondered the propriety of a warden dining on illegal venison, and tried to dismiss it in favor of the bear incident. A warden after all might expect situations of rather extenuating circumstances.

After supper he made out the rather complex report required by his superiors. Mrs. Campbell, reliving the frightening incident, was excited beyond coherence and, prompted by Spike's boastful interjections, the facts unfolded in rather jerky composition. Chet would, of course, rewrite it under calmer conditions later. Meanwhile he accumulated the facts and, having some compunction over the illegal though appetizing repast, he chafed under the couple's continuing volubility and departed as quickly as good but impatient manners permitted.

Chet's uneasiness over the affair was in no wise alleviated when, a few days later, he received a curt letter from his superior acknowledging the report of the bear incident but asking further pertinent questions. How did it happen that Mr. Campbell had a rifle in the jalopy when he returned to the bear beleaguered cabin? Why was the rifle loaded? Did Chet know that one of the strictest laws of conservation was the prohibition against carrying firearms in vehicles except if completely dismantled? Did he know that during a certain period which included that of the bear incident it was against the law to carry such firearms in game areas under any conditions?

That night Chet slept fitfully, awakening often in uneasy self-recrimination over his failure to have thought of these important details. It was early morning when he awakened from a thoroughly frightening dream in which appeared the startling apparition of his superior looking over his shoulder as he reached for another helping of lusciously spiced ground venison patties.

Conscious guilt found solace in earnest resolve. By the time Chet's breakfast was over and he was joggling on the road to Britain Bay, the resolutions born of his restless night had taken decisive action. He would henceforth be thoroughly objective in every phase of the multitudinous reports he was required to make. And he would make a thorough investigation of local game law observance which the Campbell incident had placed in a suspicious light.

Like a new broom wielded by a probationary sweeper seeking revealing dusty corners, Chet unearthed the dubious activities of the Crawfords, Indian Pete, and a host of others. He set about to obtain evidence that would warrant and sustain arrests, and he ran up against ingenious liaison, impassive evasion, and trickery that seemed to defeat his every effort—and for which the manual had not prepared him. And it was that time of the year when the deer showed the reddish sheen of their coats against the forest green in the cool dark leafy bowers of the woodland, and venison was at its best.

Violators, he soon found out, there were many. To apprehend them was like reaching into a bucket of wriggling minnows and coming up with a tiny silver sliver in an extreme comatose state. Chet caught up with a few petty miscreants while the big fry escaped his meshes. As if this were not enough, he suffered defeat in his prosecutions by loopholes and subterfuges or he faced justices whose philosophy was patterned after the preachments of the late Father Dunnegan. Those of Chet's informants who had contributed so generously to his hitherto brilliant record were now leading him on wild goose chases and into delusory dead ends. Humiliation and frustration were Chet's lot.

There was the time that he saw Red Crawford slink into the Big Cedar Swamp at dusk carrying from all appearances a long flashlight and a rifle, the necessary accoutrements for shining deer. When Red finally settled himself comfortably on a lean-to log well within the swamp area, Chet, who had trailed him, dropped on the dank soft earth behind a rotting stump and kept a miserable vigil all through a mosquito infested but moonlit night. At dawn's break Red rose, tossed away a crude walking stick and a tightly rolled newspaper, and walked abruptly to Chet's hiding place.

With shameless boldness and a derisive grin, he offered Chet the remains of a bottle of mosquito lotion, saying, "For this kinda business you oughter carry some."

Chet's wounded vanity and swollen face were in no wise assuaged by the curious glances and amused greetings that morning at Sanderson's General Store, nor by the discovery of a fresh deer hide in the back of his pickup.

Only the advent of the legal open season for upland game followed by that for waterfowl and deer saved Chet from ignominy or further victimizing. The influx of hunters from *below* kept him busily engaged in the examination of licenses and the routine observation of game law compliance, but in his spare moments he pondered gloomily his personal dilemma.

Chet had been on duty just six months. In that brief period he had learned intimately the byways of this remote hinterland, its hidden coves and lakes, and its forest bowered streams. In that six months he had won—and lost—the friendship and cooperation of its people. He would, he thought, resign and hope for an opportunity to start anew.

.   .   .

It was the morning of the last day of the deer season. Eric Klomenon was standing at the window of his log bar room looking out on the fresh tracking snow that had covered the gravel roadway. Indian Pete and Hank Lieneaux were having an early morning beer.

"De hunters is mostly gone," Eric remarked, "and now look at de trackin' snow dey was all belly-achin' for."

"Good thing they went early," replied Hank, "or else we wouldn't have a doe left. I go out on my trap line and what do I find? Does, dead does, lots of 'em, and doe fawns too. Them guys come up from *below* and shoot everything that looks like a deer. If it ain't got horns they leave it lay for the coyotes to eat and keep on shootin' until by accident one's got horns. Then they throw it on their fender and beat it for *below* to brag about what great hunters they are. And up here we got dead does and fawns. If one of us shoots us a doe outta season, what happens? That kid warden pinches us. Them guys wid lotsa money come up to raise hell for fifteen days and for every doe one of us kills outta season they knock down a dozen. By and by there won't be no deer and then wot we goin' to do for meat?"

A car slowed down before the tavern driveway and then, as if uncertain of direction, it picked its way carefully through the unbroken snow on the roadway of the left fork toward Bald Point. Eric grunted, "Der goes dem tough guys agin. Been here all season pickin' fights and shootin' crap. Never seed 'em wid a deer yet, but dey comes every season reguler." Watching the car thread its way to disappear in the winding, forest bordered trail, he added, "Never did like dere looks."

Hank, unwilling to drop a subject he liked to argue about, resumed his tirade. "Take pike spearing come spring. Them pike is so many they kin hardly find spawning room up the creeks. We go out and spear us a few and what happens? We git pinched. Come summer and them market fishermen throw nets across the island and the pike can't get in no ways. It ain't right for us to help ourselfs, but it's okay for them pirates to keep 'em out of the bays come open season. What happens? The tourists come up to fish and fishin's lousy and up to Canada they go and for us business is on the rocks."

As Hank emptied his bottle and rose, he added, "Conservation may be alright, but what good are kids like that guy Chet they sent here?"

"Aw, Chet's okay," Eric interjected, "he got bosses dat tell 'im wot to do. Don't blame him." Then, as if to change the subject, he continued, "Bin lotsa bucks stole outta camps nights. Coupla guys here last night had two swiped from where dey hung 'em in a tree and night before two guys was parked out front, two bucks on der fenders. And while dey was in here gittin' a beer somebody swipes the bucks. Hell of a note, ain't it?"

Further conversation was interrupted by hunters stopping in to have a last drink before their departure from the island and to swap small talk about the hunting season. Hank left and Indian Pete settled down behind the stove for a nap.

For Eric it had been a poor season. The hunting crowd had thinned out early in the fifteen day period and even at its peak they had spent sparingly. Throughout this last day business lagged and by late afternoon Eric was looking gloomily out of the window. On the Bald Point trail the tracks of the early morning vehicle were still visible and alone on the fresh snow. "What you spose dem bums is up to? Bin dere all day," he muttered to himself, and then he set about his daily chore, lighting the kerosene lanterns for nightfall.

As Eric was hanging the outside lantern in the entrance way, a pickup clattered by and disappeared up the left fork toward Bald Point. Looks like Chet's car, he thought, and then, walking out to the roadway, he peered at the tire tracks. Upon seeing the familiar knobby tread, he pondered the errand which was taking Chet to that lonely spot at this late hour.

As Eric returned to the bar, Hank entered and stood warming himself at the big wood burning stove. "See Chet go Bald Point way," he said. Eric nodded. In the lamplit gloom of the log bar room there was silence.

In the large spaces of the north deer country, the horde of red coated hunters are absorbed in the vastness of an area devoid of communication services and often far from travelled roads and trails. The Conservation Commission is besieged by calls from the hunters' distant homes seeking to relay emergency messages to husbands or other relatives encamped in the remote forests. To simplify the delivery of such calls, hunters are asked to register their location and most of them do so with at least a rough idea of their situation and intent. It then becomes the task of the wardens in case of need to find them.

Chet had an emergency message for a hunter whose registration indicated his intention to hunt in the Bald Point area and to camp on Shelter Bay. As Chet bumped over the frozen, rutted road surface, he noted the car tracks of an earlier vehicle on the snow. Night was falling swiftly when he reached the fork leading off to Shelter Bay. The earlier tracks led the other way toward Lost Cove. After a few hundred yards the roadway became impassable and there Chet stopped his car and went ahead on foot, until he stood on the shore line.

He followed the beach and looked at several camp sites and hunting shacks, but they were dark and empty. By the time he had reached the rocky tip of Bald Point the full moon had lighted Island Bay and the headlands of the distant shores showed dark and somber on the night's horizon. Having had no success so far, Chet decided to follow the heavily forested shore line of Lost Cove in further search, and there to cut across to the Lost Cove fork of the Bald Point trail.

It was a beautiful night. The bay was quiet and the moon reflected from the silken surface of the still water and from the clean white snow covering the beach. On the right stood the dark wall of the dense pine forest and high above, the towering limestone cliffs loomed prominently against the night sky. It was a long walk. Reaching the inner curve of the cove Chet sat down to rest, and to contemplate the peaceful wilderness scene before him.

Barely a hundred yards ahead he saw a cautious beam of light sweep the forest rim. Two rifle shots rang out, as close together as if they were one. Carefully Chet skirted the tree line, to come all too suddenly upon three men leaning over the carcass of a fallen deer.

At Chet's command they straightened up, visibly startled. But before he could move a step a fourth leaped upon him from behind, pinning him on the hard, rock strewn beach. Quickly the four removed his boots and pants, tossed them along with his service pistol and badge into the bay, and disappeared into the forest.

Dazed and bewildered, Chet struggled to his feet. It was an hour before he reached the pickup truck, only to find its four tires flattened and its gas tank punctured with a rifle bullet. He sank despondently to the running board of the useless vehicle. It was eight miles to Eric's place, the nearest habitation. As if he had not already suffered sufficient humiliation, he would now face the derisive laughter of the island folk by emerging from the forest without pants or boots and on foot. Far better that he spend the night in the woods and tomorrow find some way to the mainland and away.

Eric was looking out of the window at the moonlit, snow covered roadway. A huge truck rumbled out of the Bald Point trail and passed quickly down the main road toward the distant ferry landing. "Dat's de furst truck load of Christmas trees I seen dis winter," he said to Hank, who in curiosity crossed to the other window to take a look.

"Big load, too, and kinda early," Hank replied.

A few moments later a car slid to a stop in front of the bar room. A swarthy man entered the building, followed by three more. Eric nudged Hank and whispered, "Dat's dem tough guys."

"What time is the next ferry?" the swarthy man asked gruffly.

Eric looked at the cheap alarm clock at the end of the bar. "You gotta whole hour," he replied.

Turning to his companions, the man said, "Got time for a couple beers."

Eric pulled the bottles out of the cooler, carefully wiped them, and set them on the bar. Then he walked across the room, tossed a chunk of wood into the stove, and shook the grates noisily. Indian Pete, lounging in the chair, awakened from the noise and stared drowsily at Eric, who leaned toward him and whispered, "Take my truck quick to de ferry an' tell dem der is some funny bizness."

Returning behind the bar, Eric set up another round for his unexpected customers and noted with satisfaction that Pete had departed through the back door.

When the men had left, Eric turned to Hank. "Chet's got trouble. You take my jeep and drive to Bald Point. You know his tracks."

Without question Hank hastened to obey.

Corky yawned as he left the warm comfort of the tiny pilot house on the ferry boat. "Time to load up," he said as he pulled down his earlaps and loosened the rope block to lower the ramp. A truck load of Christmas trees pulled up and Corky motioned its driver to come on board. Eric's truck came down the hill road, pulled to one side, and Indian Pete walked aboard the ferry and whispered to Corky. Grinning, Corky stuck his head through the window of the pilot house and spoke briefly to the pilot, who grinned in turn and nodded his head.

In a few minutes the car containing the four men rolled to a stop and Corky waved them on. After chocking carefully the wheels of the big truck and the passenger car, he raised the ramp to closed position for departure and returned to the warmth of the pilot house.

For half an hour the two crewmen lounged in comfort on the cushioned bench, reading comic magazines and glancing occasionally at the four men sitting in the passenger car. The men showed signs of agitated impatience, and the driver finally got out. Opening the pilot house door, he inquired, "Hey Bud, when do we leave?"

Corky unconcernedly replied, "Dunno. Engine won't start," and he continued his perusal of the comics.

The swarthy man paced the deck impatiently, his state

of agitation increasing by the minute. In obvious anger he again addressed the crew, asking gruffly, "When you think you going to get the engine fixed?"

"Dunno," replied Corky and then, in apparent annoyance at the disturbance, he closed the door and locked it.

Another half an hour went by, and by this time all four were pacing the deck, gesticulating angrily at each other, muttering low voiced profanity, and casting meaningful glances at the unconcerned crew. Corky and the pilot, having exhausted the comic book supply, were playing cribbage. The truck driver was sound asleep.

A car popped over the hill and, as its headlights swung into range, it blinked them three times. Corky and the pilot rose and walked out on deck. The swarthy man growled, "Who are they?"

Corky, grinning from ear to ear, replied, "Oh them? They's the guys to fix the engine."

The jeep came to a sliding halt only a few feet from the ramp. Eric and Hank climbed out, followed by Chet wearing undersize pants and oversize boots. All three carried rifles.

Without a word, Corky lowered the ramp for them to come aboard. At the same instant the pilot started the engine.

Hearing the rumble of the exhaust, the foursome was startled beyond words. They made a run for the lowered ramp, only to look into three levelled rifles and behind them three grinning faces.

Chet frisked them quickly, and while Eric and Hank held them to the rail, he removed the firearms from their vehicle. Then, ordering them into their car, Chet signalled the pilot to cast loose. As he did so the truck driver awakened and with a frightened glance at the activity on the deck he leaped from his seat. Hank swung his rifle toward him, saying, "What you so scared about, buddy?"

Corky, still grinning, answered for him. "Look under the Christmas trees."

Eric and Hank began throwing the trees overboard as the little ferry headed toward the mainland. By the time it had tied up to its pier, they had dug out from balsam scented concealment eight antlered deer and an equal number of illegal does.

Eric nodded his head knowingly, "Der's dem bucks dat was swiped. Dey got der deer tags on em."

.   .   .

Chet spent the winter down *below* taking a refresher course in conservation. If he still entertained the thought of resigning, he was in no hurry to translate it into action. Spring's arrival brought reassignment to his last year's district and in high spirits he headed his little pickup northward to the scenes of his greatest humiliations—and triumphs.

The Bald Point episode afforded the winter weary islanders a topic of conversation for long, snowbound evenings, and especially so around the big wood burning stove that contributed warmth and comfort to match the conviviality of Eric's bar room. It had been a long, hard winter.

The spring breakup had been slow and tardy and the frost boiled roads rutted deeply and were often impassable. April showers came late but, aided by a warm though infrequent sun, they beat back the stubborn snow to scant fringes in the sheltered depths of the dense woodland. Early spring flowers struggled bravely in the performance of their brief but decorative role, and pussy willows flaunted their silken buds in defiance of the recurring frosts.

The silvery smelt, prompted by the rising water temperatures and springtime urge, left the dark depths of Island Bay and headed toward the streams and rivers to lay their spawn and propagate their species. They came first in scattered groups, gliding quietly up the currents and back again as if to probe the timeliness of their seasonal pilgrimage to the sandy bottoms of brooks and streams and water courses. Then, as if the aggregate of favorable conditions was by some inexplicable means announced in concert, the teeming hordes, waiting restlessly in the green waters of the surging bay, rushed in mysterious unity, darting and leaping in countless swarms in a mad effort to reach their distant rendezvous up swiftly flowing streams.

Whatever the inexorable impulse that prompts this annual peregrination of the denizens of the deep, the big smelt run came as a welcome diversion to the good folks of the land *above below*. Wearied by the tedious dullness of a seemingly endless winter, to them the silvery fish brought feast and frolic and a resumption of rustic social communion.

When, after the few nights of the run, the streams would return to the normal quiet of sandy bottoms and gurgling ripples, and the budding alders would change the brown drabness of winter to high lighted green and reddened brown, an equally phenomenal migration would take place. This time it would not be the slender, silver smelt in multitudinous hordes, but instead the long northern pike, fighting fish of the rush grown bays, who would push their horny snouts through the grassy bottoms and marshy bogs, alert to the spearman waiting in lantern lit gloom on the marshy shores.

And overhead would be the loitering waterfowl on their northward trek—mallards, geese, and teal and butterballs—their winter sojourn done, and now bound for harsher climes to rear more of their kind.

In the woods the deer would find green browse, fresh moss, and budding morsels. Their winter leanness would give way to curving grace, and last year's fawns would gain the firmness of flesh and the tenderness that makes for luscious stew.

It is small wonder that to remote cabins, logging camps, and lesser abodes there should come a common urge for festive fun, for get-togethers, to eat and drink and frolic.

Eric got the idea first, but its prompt endorsement indicated that others thought that way too. Why not have a huge game dinner, with french fried smelt, broiled fresh pike, roast goose and duck, and venison stew? Out of season? Well, who cares?

And so it was. On rutted roads, on foot and wheel, they came from coves and bays and points. There were woodsmen, loggers, fishermen, guides, carpenters, laborers, and bartenders too. There were Finns and Scots and Swedes and Poles and Frenchmen and Indians and Englishmen. Eric's bar room nearly burst its mud caulked seams as they milled around, or sat on tables, chairs, and logs, or sprawled in chatty groups upon the floor. Wood smoke mingled with the enticing smells of fish and fowl, of bakery goods and spicy, piquant venison stew.

It was by chance that just as Eric raised his voice to call them to line up and help themselves, Indian Pete rushed in breathlessly to announce that Corky had sent word that the lid was on—Chet had just crossed over on the ferry and was coming this way.

They still talk about that affair in the land *above below*, but not very explicitly. The women say that Chet liked the roast duck better than the venison, but there are others who say his preference was for goose, and then again it was the stew. The one point they all seem to agree upon is that Chet liked everything better than the smelt because the smelt were legal, and that from the way he ate he couldn't have been eating regularly the winter he went *below*. Others just smile and say, "Chet? Oh, he's a nice guy."

When Eric is asked, he just sort of grins and says, "Chet's a shwell feller, but he can't hold much beer."

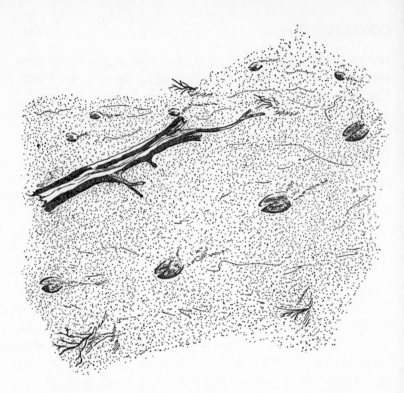

HUNTERS' BALL

Ed Brandon dumped the greasy contents of a smoke black-ened skillet into a bucket beside the old-fashioned, wood burning cook stove. Bill Miller stumbled from the blustery darkness outside into the lantern lit dimness of the hunting shack, stamped his feet viciously to rid them of clinging flakes, and walked noisily to the stove, carrying two pails packed tightly with snow.

The wind from the open door provoked the ancient range to give forth a cloud of acrid smoke, which in turn brought a mildly profane reproof from Ed. The admonition was lost, however, in a burst of spitting and sizzling and a clanking protest from the frail stove lids as Bill plunked the two pails on the cherry red surface of the stove.

"There, by God, that ought to give us enough water for the dishes and some left over for coffee in the morning." Then, without further words, Bill reached for the ragged remnant of a discarded undershirt and waited patiently to wipe the dishes.

Ed looked at the brownish water in the dishpan, barely covering a filthy array of cups, plates, knives, and forks, and scowled with ill-concealed disgust at the distasteful task before him. "Cripes," he growled, "that ain't enough water to wash this crap."

Seating himself on a crude chair, Ed lit a cigarette and continued, "Guess I better wait till that damned snow gets melted."

Bill, thankful for the welcome reprieve, tossed himself on a jumble of blankets over an unmade canvas cot, and gave vent to groans and grunts and expressions of great fatigue. To this Ed added an "Amen" and together they puffed at their cigarettes in silence.

They might well be tired. On this their fifth day of the deer season, they had tramped miles through knee deep snow, and sat for hours shivering in painful alertness, watching the runways for the furtive buck to show his antlered head. So far, no luck.

A week before, they had crossed the water barrier from *below*, and after a few hours of smooth concrete, had turned their car onto the uncertainty and roughness of lumbering roads. After two hours that had seemed an eternity, they had unloaded their supplies and carried them into the rough board shack.

The remainder of the afternoon and all the next day had been spent in cutting firewood and in rehabilitating the primitive quarters, including the ancient stove. They had had to dispossess a family of full grown mice, repair damages wrought by a couple of enterprising porcupines, and seal a multitude of leaks in the aging roof.

They had gone about their tasks joyously and with enthusiasm. This was the vacation for which they had toiled all year in the confining dullness of office and shop in the noisome, cavernous Motor City *below*. This was escape, adventure, excitement, relaxation—this was the call of the wild.

Their work done, they had flopped happily into their hard, unyielding bunks and, forgetting care and worry and responsibility, had fallen quickly asleep in an aura of exquisite anticipation, soothed by the softly falling, feathery snowflakes. Tomorrow the season would begin, and there would be tracking snow.

And now five days had passed. The deer were plentiful, but they were wise, too. But no matter, there were still ten days to go, ten days of tracking, stalking, of exhilarating exposure to frosty air, of association with the spruce spires, lofty pine, and the seemingly endless forests. There were still ten days of flapjacks and hot coffee, of canned beans and soups, and of sourdough biscuits. There were still ten days of pleasant weariness and delicious dreamless sleep. And there were still ten days of scraping greasy, smoke blackened frying pans, of washing dishes in dirty brown water, of coaxing a stubborn, smoky stove, and of staying the persistent pangs of incipient dejection.

These past days had tempered their enthusiasm. Accustomed to the amenities of modern conveniences designed for gracious and comfortable living, it is small wonder that a reversion to the austerity of backwoods living would soon dampen their zest for exciting adventure and somewhat decrease, but by no means banish, their appetites for the arduous pursuit of the elusive deer. If doubt in the genuineness of their desire to emulate the deeds of frontier huntsmen entered into the reluctance with which they now prosecuted the task of washing dishes, it was perhaps abetted by the persistent fantasy of the culinary products of a gentler urban atmosphere and its attendant comforts.

They were perhaps unaware that they were not alone the victims of this lessening of enthusiasm. All over this country of forested spaces were thousands of other wouldbe Nimrods whose fervency had been dimmed by exposure to the harshness of elemental rusticity too suddenly applied and too prolonged.

Ed poured hot water over the dishes, reached for a cake of yellow soap, and winced as he put his hands into the unaccustomed heat. Bill got slowly to his feet, reached for his makeshift dish towel, and disdainfully applied himself to the odious task of wiping dishes.

As Ed laid out the last utensil and began desultorily to wipe the dishpan, he said with more suggestion than question, "How far is it to the Birch Bark Tavern?"

Bill replied with briskness and obvious inspiration, reacting more to the suggestion than the question, "About an hour over on the Black River Road, two miles off the concrete. Wanta go?"

"Be kinda nice—might be sumpthin doin over there."

The alacrity with which the remaining domestic tasks were accomplished is proof of the infectiousness of inspired and enthusiastic anticipation, and the need for gregarious conviviality—even in the manful response to the call of the chase.

.   .   .

Mike Tovarsin, a roly-poly Finn and the proprietor of the backwoods Birch Bark Tavern, knew well the instincts and habits of the red coated invaders from *below*, and therefore he prepared well for them. He knew that the horde would arrive a day or two before the season and spend these days in feverish preparation of their camp sites. He knew that on the opening day at break of dawn they would over-run the nooks and trails and runways in clumsy haste, sorely infected with buck fever and impatience. By night the aches and pains, the strains of unused muscles, and the un-accustomed exertion would drive them to their bunks in de-licious weariness, to rise again after deep, unbroken slumber to hopeful and continued pursuit.

About the fifth or sixth day, flesh and spirit would re-bel against the fruitless torture, and wisdom of experience would calm the impetuous urge to a saner and more pro-ductive pace. Mike knew also that about that time "dem boys," as he was wont to call them, would be thinking about mixing a little conviviality with the otherwise gruelling though exciting routine. And this was the night.

The little lighting plant had been tuned and checked for dependable performance; but lanterns and candles stra-tegically located indicated that, even then, this service was not assured. Beer cases had been stacked high along the side walls of the spacious beer hall to inspire confidence and promote the desire for abundance.

The ancient juke box had been pushed out so that its position coincided with the area of greatest traffic, namely in the path that led from the bar to the significantly marked vestibules for "Setters" and "Pointers." Mike knew well how many nickels could be coaxed into juke box circula-tion by this arrangement.

Extra pine board tables and benches had been retrieved from the woodshed and firewood had been stored in a cord-wood manner to stoke the great sheet iron stove. This served a double function—that of supply and safety—the latter indicating the probability of celebrants out of control and lacking in equilibrium.

Drinking tables offered much profit, dancing space little if any, so a very limited area had been left open for the latter. But this had been well waxed to please those who craved some rompish diversion.

Bottled liquor had been stacked behind glass doors under lock and key, labels facing invitingly outward. This arrangement differed from the usual, since only bonded and expensive brands were visible. Mike's native patronage indulged only in cheaper brands and in consequence his inventory accumulation of bonded and higher priced liquor often pinched his working capital. The "whiskey at any price" hunting crowd might question the paucity of lower priced fire water, but only long enough to buy what was on the shelf. Natives were provided for during the deer season by an ingenious under the counter service.

Having experienced over many years the uninhibited playfulness of an "on the loose" sporting crowd, Mike had placed a small table and chair at the entrance, and had prominently displayed a sign reading "Check your hunting knives here." This precaution was commendatory to the depth of Mike's wise experience. The rather intriguing, if not attractive, Indian girl who presided over the table indicated deep insight into human qualities, particularly those of deer hunters.

Lacking was the familiar bouncer or strong-arm defender of propriety and property. This was not an oversight. Mike knew well that, as the evening crowd swelled, there would be for every pleasure bent hunter a native to watch the fun. Since most of the natives were of lumberjack proportions, the question of establishing order if need be was well taken care of, including that among the lumberjacks themselves.

The colorful crowd trickled in slowly by twos and threes. Veterans of past years shook hands with Mike, who in turn greeted them boisterously as if they were old friends. It mattered not that he frequently had to inquire of the bar-keeper, "Who was dat guy? He knows me but I ain't never seen him before."

By the time the crowd had reached a scant dozen, the juke box began its assault on conversational possibilities, and voices were raised to more competitive levels. A four-some of lumberjacks arrived and started a game of rummy, and the perennial kibitzers moved in for a look at the game. A few Indians arrived, and the pinball machine claimed them. Hunters stood around watching, curious to learn if their racial origin possessed them of any exceptional skill in operating this purely mechanical contrivance.

Now and then a woman would arrive, usually accom-panied, occasionally native, but more often a Nimrod of the gentler sex. If the latter, she wore red plaid garments in all respects similar to those of the other hunters. Sex, age, and degree of charm were in consequence difficult to determine, but every male spotted the women on arrival, probably mak-ing a mental note to try out the waxed floor surface later. If by chance a female arrival was Indian, increased interest and curiosity were displayed, while the natives on the other hand paid no heed.

Mike's sales were on a self-serve basis or, more pre-cisely, a come and get it and pay when you get it plan. Serv-ing only bottled beer and packaged liquor, the capacity of one barkeeper to wait on the crowd was prodigious. A tall, gaunt Indian was kept busy gathering up empty bottles and carrying them to the rear of the bar. It might be questioned whether the promptness with which empties were retrieved was in the interest of their return value, or as a precautionary arrangement to prevent their use as playful missiles.

By now the outer door opened oftener and to the accompaniment of stamping feet and shouts of recognition. By the time the first barber shop quartette attempted feebly to penetrate the clamor with questionable harmony, the door was more often open than closed. The trickle was now an avalanche, as from distant hunting camps the Eds and Bills, the Johns and Georges, and all the other eager Nimrods succumbed to their social instincts and flocked in search of conviviality. This would be a hunters' ball, unheralded and unplanned. No neon lights or gaudy advertising proclaimed its offering of cheer and merrymaking. It was born of a spontaneous revulsion to greasy skillets and dirty dishes and unyielding beds, of surrender to the protest of aching, tired muscles, and of reluctant admission of a waning appetite for the adventure of the chase. This was a chance to raise hell and let hair down in unabashed and uninhibited celebration. This was the stimulating shot in the arm that would send the Redcoats back with renewed ardor for the rigors of the hunt, and a kindlier attitude toward stubborn stoves and improvised dishrags and flapjacks and canned beans.

Mike beamed as he surveyed the swelling crowd from his vantage post at the cash register. The successful hunters, those who "got their buck," could be easily identified. They went from table to table and from booth to booth with a bottle of whiskey, treating the crowd. Wherever the opportunity presented itself, they would loudly boast of their sharpshooting prowess. Always theirs was the biggest, the fleetest, the most elusive buck.

The hunters were now drinking straight whiskey washed down with beer, a custom packed with high potentiality and copied from the natives, who were more inured to its disastrous effects.

When an eminent big town banker in the far corner raised his voice in a raucous Indian love call and was answered by a prominent architect in the opposite corner with what might have been a coalescence of a wolf howl, a war cry, and a yodel, Mike knew that the crowd was getting in gear. Barber shop quartettes of assorted quality had by now sprung up in several booths. A few couples were risking the hazards of collision by venturing out on the waxed dance area and seeking vainly to identify the cadence of the juke box in the babble of song, table pounding, and whooping.

The natives had shed their polite aloofness and, inspired by inward warmth, joined in the fun with reckless abandon. The Indians caught the spirit too.

"Chust look at dem boys spend money," Mike said to his barkeeper and, noticing the man's bleary nod, he hastened to summon the relief man. The barkeeper had caught the spirit too, and before the festivities would come to a crashing close, Mike would need to summon often.

The crowd was now beginning to circulate. Intimate groups were breaking up to form again with strangers. Mike knew what this meant, so he began his mingling, bottle on the hip and alert for danger signs.

Loud talking drew him toward a group being entertained by a blustering drunk who sought battle and loudly proclaimed his intention. Mike's technique was perfect. He invited him to a private drink, and such an invitation coming from the proprietor appealed to the whiskey inspired ego of the would-be belligerent. But when Mike offers a private drink, its potency is usually calculated to appease the bellicose tendencies of the recipient and to promote a desire for undisturbed slumber so deep that a hardwood floor with a stick of wood for a pillow is as acceptable as an innerspring mattress. Mike calls this his "finishing" process, and before the evening was over, he would have to "finish" several.

Near the outer door, the Indian girl custodian of the sheath knives was being propositioned by an inebriated but ambitious hunter who, presuming aboriginal limitations, was seeking to make himself understood in sign language, much to the amusement of the Indians who were watching the process. A rum and coke mixture of a great deal of rum and very little coke laid him low, a precaution suggested to Mike by the presence of the girl's husband in the group of interested onlookers.

Meanwhile, a few of the celebrants had passed out voluntarily, and Mike's close lumberjack friends were needed to dispose of them so that the limited floor space might not suffer in consequence.

From intermingling crowds come strange combinations. A yellow haired down-stater had joined a center table occupied by two Indian couples, and presently the group was increased by yet another paleface. Mike made a mental note of this situation, for experience had taught him that such incongruous groups bore watching. The temperamental variety, added to their state of intoxication, was explosive.

Somebody suggested a square dance, but its execution suffered from limited space and the injection of tango, polka, and schottische dance movements. Its conclusion was such an uproarious comedy that everyone wanted to join in a repeat performance. This had the unfortunate tendency of breaking up chummy groups, upsetting tables, and furrowing Mike's brows deeper with increased apprehension. Beer bottles were now being kicked around the floor like hockey pucks and soon someone would feel inspired to exhibit his baseball prowess.

But the attention of the crowd was momentarily drawn to a three ring dancing circus. A middle-aged female Nimrod, clad in scarlet, was performing her version of Salome's art on the top of a wiggly table. The second attraction was a pair putting on an altogether too realistic exhibition of a Parisian Apache dance; the male performer in this instance was brandishing a sheath knife which he had evidently failed to check at the entrance. The third ring was the yellow haired interloper at the center table who, for the benefit of his aboriginal friends was going through a frenzied Indian war dance to a tom-tom accompaniment, produced by rapping the floor with a pair of beer bottles, and punctuated by shrill utterances in the best tradition of battle bound and murderous savages. Mike did not like the stony disinterest of the Indian couples, particularly of the men. Here was a situation that needed plenty of attention.

Meanwhile the aspirant to Salome honors had removed her jacket and was unbuttoning her blouse. Mike eyed the situation warily until he was satisfied that the purpose was for cooling rather than for a strip tease.

Mike then returned to the center table laden with a tray of explosive rum drinks and noted with satisfaction that the effect was immediate, if only temporary.

By now a would-be orator had mounted an improvised rostrum; in the smoky murk and deafening din he brandished a beer bottle to give emphasis to the controversial subject of prohibition. Someone obligingly tipped the juke box for a rendition of the "Beer Barrel Polka," at the same time turning up its volume to ear splitting distortion. Bent on being heard and permitting no competition, the would-be orator hurled the bottle so accurately that, so far as this night's festivities were concerned, the mechanical entertainer was *hors de combat.*

It was way past closing time but, because of the location of the Birch Bark Tavern, Mike feared no complaint from law enforcement agencies. Nevertheless, the beer bottle episode indicated the advisability of an early termination to this conviviality that was rapidly getting beyond control. That this would be difficult Mike knew from the past. It needed some culminating incident to end it, and sometimes such incidents were neither pleasant nor entertaining. Mike hoped that it would not be a free-for-all.

The fire had already been permitted to burn itself out, but the atmosphere had not yet chilled sufficiently to cause a general exodus. A few had left, and a few more had entertained the notion, but the swirling snow outside abetted a general reluctance to leave.

Meanwhile unusual interest was being displayed in the direction of the center table. Mike decided to investigate. What he saw transfixed him with perplexed terror and dismay.

With brazen disregard for an amused audience of a hundred odd celebrants, Yellow Hair was making unabashed love to the two Indian women, fondling both in ardent embrace. A crow-black head nestled on each of his shoulders in comical contrast to his straw colored locks, and return caresses suggested receptive warmth and tractability. Across the table, glaring in angry disapproval, sat their husbands. Mike knew that only their extreme drunken stupor stayed a most savage retaliation, and for the moment only.

He also knew that the two recipients of Yellow Hair's favors would soon explode in a violent exhibition of rivalry with consequences unpredictable and unmanageable.

By the time Mike had collected his thoughts sufficiently to think of some appeasing action, both husbands had risen. They staggered forward with murderous resolve and brandished chairs, only to collide and sprawl in a drunken heap.

The amorous ladies, resenting this attempted assault upon their fair haired Adonis, leaped shrieking upon them; with fury preserved only for the female of the species, they inflicted an eye-gouging, nail-scratching, hair-pulling punishment which, if state of inebriation had permitted, would have caused any pair of wronged husbands to retreat in utter abandonment of any defense of family honor. Not so these two. While the cheering audience climbed tables and chairs for better vantage points, the two men recovered their sobriety with remarkable speed and seized their women in a most secure fashion. Unmindful of the generous display of anatomy, they administered a flat handed whipping so vehement that it smacked above the uproar of the appreciative onlookers.

Then, with evident mastery of the situation, they seized the shrieking and sobbing women in a strong grip above and below and steered them to the exit door in single file. With one vicious and accurately aimed kick, they pitched the disheveled pair headlong into the snowbank outside. The crowd surged forward.

A whimpering pair of wives picked themselves out of the bright snow under the entrance floodlight. There remained no desire for punitive action against their husbands and most certainly no appetite for a return engagement. Their hair wildly matted with snow and their clothing in disarray, they presented a contrite, as well as amusing, picture. In their state of docility they could have been propelled homeward without protest, content perhaps to have escaped a more severe fate.

The husbands, however, were not of a mind to allow the amorous pursuer to escape a similar ignominious chastisement. They returned to the center table.

Yellow Hair was easy to handle—a beer bottle in full flight, added to his extreme state of intoxication, rendering him most tractable. Together they pitched him out the door to land headlong between the women, there to exhibit none of his wolfish tendencies, nor any of his bold amorous advances, but to proclaim by loud and sobbing lamentations the injustice of it all.

This provoked uproarious laughter among the spectators but the women, swaying with uncertainty and fear of further marital punishment, were moved to compassion. With a common protective impulse they leaped toward their lover but, each sensing the other's intention, they paused to glare in furious rivalry. The green-eyed monster triumphed. With screaming invective they swung at each other, missed, and launched into a hair-pulling melee of such fury as to be individually indefinable. The crowd loved it. Coats, hats, and bottles were grabbed in one wild rush through the exit where the spectators formed a solid ring around the flailing combatants and shouted encouragement to them.

Mike surveyed his empty and disordered beer hall. Quickly he closed and bolted the door and nodded to his barkeeper. Lights dimmed and then went out as the exhaust of the lighting plant sputtered to a stop. Darkness prevailed, and another hunters' ball was over.

.   .   .

It was late morning when Ed carefully raised one eye over the edge of his blanket and looked over the foot of his cot toward the other bunk. He found Bill employing a similar strategy. Reaching for a coin he flipped it and as it spun in its descent, Bill called for heads and lost.

Ed sank cozily back into the warmth of his blankets as Bill sprang up to make good his loss. He kindled the fire, set the kettle to boil, and, as he vigorously stirred the batch of flapjack batter, he whistled a lively tune.

An hour later, in a lingering aroma of hotcakes and coffee, and with the domestic chores neatly attended to, they strode forth from their shack into the furry white of the forest, their rifles cradled under their arms. The balsam boughs bent low with the weight of newly fallen snow, while white flakes parachuted softly about them.

"Boy, this is the life!" said Bill in a tone that left no doubt of his sincerity.

In complete agreement, Ed answered, "And we got ten whole days left!"

SANCTUARY

SLIM CRAWFORD, the blackest sheep of the Crawford clan and a perennial thorn in the side of the conservation officers in their conscientious protection of wild life, nosed his leaky flatboat into the rushes of Middle Cove. Reaching the shallows, he removed one oar and poled his way toward the weeded beach. He stepped on shore, pulled the craft high above the water line, and carefully stowed his oars behind a clump of ground balsam.

A moment later he rested from his exertions on a flat rock concealed by dense cedar. His position afforded him a view of the line where the dense growth of the trees gave way to the rush grown, marshy beach.

It was a lovely August morning. The sun, but a few hours high in the blue dome of a faultless sky, promised a mid-summer day unruffled by wind or cloud. For several hundred feet the tall rushes protruded high and dense above the water. They thinned gradually toward the glassy outlines of the open cove to reflect a pleasing pattern upon the tranquil calm.

Here and there the rushes would bend as if impelled by unseen hands, and into the quiet of the glassy surface a mother duck and her fluffy brood would weave a triangular pattern of glistening ripples.

A lone blue heron in quest of an early morning breakfast stood like a statue on a sandy projection rimmed by an array of water-worn boulders, while gliding noiselessly in play a pair of half grown mink cut ruffled circles, as if they too were actors in a lovely wilderness drama.

From the denseness of the great forest bordering the unspoiled and natural beauty of the cove came the soft and soothing sounds of wild life busy with its morning chores.

Great birches broke the deep green of the forest curtain, leaning away from its denseness, the bright green of their freshened leaves and the white of their bark contrasting with the grassy fringe and the soft darkness of the spruce and balsam. It was fitting and proper that the trunk of a huge pine, standing apart sentinel-like, displayed a prominent sign proclaiming this sylvan scene with its surrounding forest and its placid cove to be reserved for all posterity as a refuge for wild life.

A poet might have been impelled to weave verse and write praise had he but sat on the flat rock vantage point occupied by the quiet and sinister figure of Slim Crawford.

But if the tableau of grace, beauty, spiritual peace, and nature's bounty stirred him to kindly emotion, it was not evident in the cruel and sardonic countenance that peered cunningly along the forest rim.

A hundred yards or so to the south a slim and graceful doe moved cautiously into the open and paused to carefully survey the shore line. Finding no trace of an enemy, she sauntered daintily down the beach, while around and under her a tiny spotted fawn pranced in the ecstasy of its infant innocence and fearlessness.

Slim watched. For an hour the doe and fawn remained within his line of vision. Speculatively he noted the trim loins and the healthy, reddish sheen of the doe's coat. Venison was at its best in August just as the coat took on that color.

Having completed the purpose of their shoreline visit, the woodland pair moved with unhurried deliberation toward the forest fringe. A moment later they disappeared into the dense growth.

Slim waited half an hour, then rose and walked to his well hidden flatboat. Then he proceeded southward, carrying a hand axe and a coil of fine wire. Carefully he scanned the tracks on the beach until he came to the alder bush where they had turned into the forest. Without stepping on the tracks he parted the bushes and took note of the ground. It was as he had thought, a hidden deer runway leading into the deep tamarack swamp a quarter of a mile distant. Paralleling the runway, he followed it back a few hundred feet, careful not to cross it or to step upon it.

When he found what he wanted, Slim laid his coil of wire on the ground and with the sharp hand axe he fashioned several stakes. Directly overhead was the large branch of a giant maple. Carefully winding and binding the wire about it he fashioned a loose loop and twisted a slip knot around its running end. Then, placing another wire on the branch, he pulled with all his weight until the branch sagged several feet below its natural position. He cut a gash into an adjacent cedar, seated a prop, and fastened the wire to it. The heavy branch was held tight in its bent position.

Noting that the deer tracks all ran in one direction, he strung his trip wires on the approach side and then concealed his handiwork with a woodsman's skill. Long experience had taught him much about the habits of does with fawns. The chore for which the white-tailed pair had sauntered shoreward would be repeated that evening or certainly by morning. Thus without the telltale report of a rifle the best of venison would be available for personal enjoyment and profit.

Judging direction without crossing the runways, Slim emerged upon the beach midway between the places where the doe and fawn had left and re-entered the forest. He returned to the flat rock and slashed an armful of balsam boughs. After arranging them into a comfortable couch, he settled himself for a pleasant nap.

The scene remained as in the morning when Slim awakened, except that the afternoon sun cast its shadows in the opposite direction. On the open cove a flock of half grown mallard ducks swam in a youthful attempt at adult flight formation. A crippled duck lagged behind and, as if fearful of its loneliness, it half flew and skidded to catch up with the family brood. High in the sky a great eagle sailed with awesome majesty surveying the wondrous area below.

Close into the rushes, a mother fish duck, its crest bobbing anxiously, watched its tiny fluffy brood cavort in the quiet water, and with rasping throaty sounds admonished them to remain close to their maternal protection.

On the slippery rocks the mink pair reclined in puppy fashion, content and comfortable in the warmth of the late afternoon sun. Now and then one would rise and with arched back dash in mock attack at its playmate who, reluctant to rise from its supine comfort, would roll over and playfully slap its paws at the disturber.

Slim watched the open water beyond the distant point that enclosed the lower bend of the cove. About sundown the white boat of the conservation officers would pass there heading for the mainland, their day's labor of vigilance completed. He could then in safety row back the several miles to Meadow Cove, a short walking distance from the shack which he called home. There was no hurry. No wife awaited him, nor had he any near neighbors. The comings and goings of Slim Crawford interested no one, except perhaps the alert and watchful guardians of the wild.

The sun sank lower and the shadows deepened. Slim sat idly, with apparent disinterest for the woodland life engaged in its daily work and pastimes. A frantic rasping cry from the fish duck brood attracted his attention. In a swirl of water a silvery streak rose and then rolled and splashed loudly as a giant fish seized a downy duckling and disappeared below the surface. The white boat should be coming about now, he thought.

To the south a hound appeared, small in stature and with the unkempt and emaciated body of a stray. He crept quietly to the sandy point rimmed by rocks. The young mink sensed his approach and crouched in alertness. Cunningly they permitted him to reach their slippery footing and, as he sprang to attack, they slid deftly into the water. The momentum of his charge carried the dog onto the surface of the rock, where he failed to gain a substantial foothold and plunged into the deep water. The mink rose from a dive and, as if in planned attack, glided in a close circle from either side. In a moment they had seized his ears and with savage dives they held his head under water until his struggling ceased.

The splashing disturbed the young mallards, who scattered in every direction in full flight to land again and join their forces on the other side of the cove. Their frantic crippled member endeavored to follow but it failed to take to wing. Plummeting from the sky, the great eagle dove with incredible precision, pinned the hapless duck, and completely submerged in the violence of the plunge. Heavily it rose to the surface, its prey clutched in its talons. With powerful wing sweeps it cleared the water and paused to shake its great body free of water. Then it rose swiftly upward and away.

The sun was lowering fast, and still the white boat did not appear. Could these officers have suspected Slim's presence in the sanctuary? Apprehension seized him. As dusk began to close in, he decided to wait no longer. He picked up the coil of remaining wire and looked around for his hand axe. With horror he realized that he had left it at the unlawful snare. This would be just the evidence the officers needed, for carved on its hickory handle were his initials.

Hurriedly he retraced his steps. He had not reckoned with the early darkness in the woods and stumbled ineptly in the undergrowth.

Reaching the runway, he looked first to the left, then to the right, in a frantic attempt to find the cunningly concealed trap. In the darkness he could just see the revealing axe. He stooped, grasped its handle, and drew it toward him. Too late. A soft swish—a violent snap—and the taut wire bit into his chest stifling his outcry as the strong branch jerked him from the ground.

The moon rose over the quiet stillness of the cove. The rushes bent gracefully and cast equally graceful reflections upon the darkened water. The rim of the forest formed a frame around the cove and night birds twittered softly, accompanied by the hum of invisible insect hordes. The white birch rose in exaggerated proportions to the forest darkness, and the sentinel pine stood silhouetted against the night sky. On the marshy beach, Slim Crawford dragged his pain-racked body toward the flatboat hidden in the rushes that lined the placid waters of Middle Cove.

THE SAINTS OF DEEP HARBOR

IT was that time of year again when no outhouse in the North Woods village of Deep Harbor could assure privacy and respect of occupancy or maintain its fixed and upright position. All Saints' Day in Deep Harbor, as in all towns, villages, and hamlets, was a day to apprehend with helpless fear and foreboding.

Deep Harbor's problem was in no wise alleviated either by its environment or the character of its juveniles of both sexes. Then too, their parents and the generations before them had a none too highly developed respect for law and order and, as a consequence, inhibited prankishness was hardly to be expected. And in no other place could be found such a variety and number of outhouses and other tempting objects of reasonable mobility.

On this particular Halloween, however, the vulnerability of the village was at its best or, from the standpoint of tranquility, at its worst. The male population of the settlement was at low ebb; there being a war on, those who were of proper age had long since departed to don uniforms, while many who were unfit by reason of age or physical condition had left to seek war time wages in areas far distant.

As a consequence, the affairs of family life were largely in the hands of the weaker sex, a qualification purely theoretical. The affairs of community life rested upon the patriarchal beer guzzlers and the shiftless loafers. This is, of course, not altogether so, since there were a few who remained to conduct the necessary community services such as barkeeping, selling groceries, and the like. At any rate there remained in Deep Harbor enough of the questionably solid citizenry to view the forthcoming anniversary of vandalism with genuine alarm and with a commendable feeling of civic responsibility. With home defenses weakened and the inherent lawlessness of unbridled teen-age exuberance, this All Saints' Day could be one that would be long remembered. Something had to be done about it.

Much informal discussion preceded any concerted plan of defense. Such discussion usually took place around the bar or the cracker barrel of the local general store. As might be expected, much unsolicited as well as questionable advice and suggestion was placed at the disposal of the strategists by well meaning and sometimes facetious listeners. Time, on the other hand, stood still for no one, and the dreaded day approached upon a defenseless, isolated community, a community without even a nominal peace officer.

The evening before the impending pillage of Deep

Harbor, Philo sat on an empty crate in front of the local post office, awaiting the distribution of the mail which had just arrived from the distant railhead. Near him lounged Jacques and Hugo. If business rivalry sometimes chilled these barkeepers' association, it was not evident in the serious discussion of the moment. They could well remember the surreptitious interchange of their beer brands in a former year, and how they had suffered the embarrassment of retrieving a truckload of empty bottles that the precocious saints of vandalism had moved into the local church basements. Nor could they forget the cascade of barnyard refuse that had descended through hot chimneys down into their pot-bellied heating stoves, hardly improving the beery aroma of their respective emporiums of thirst quenching. The upset of their tavern privies was an annually expected affair, but to get them off the neighbor's roof called for physical exertion beyond the capacity of their bar room softness. They could accept, perhaps, the flattened tires of their ancient vehicles, and even the reversal of ignition wires, but gasoline tanks stuffed full with overripe tomatoes, axle grease on steering wheels, disconnected mufflers, and short circuited horns were enough to drive any group of tavern keepers into a most drastic conspiracy for defense.

And so, early that evening in the dilapidated and miniature town hall, Philo, Jacques, and Hugo sat at the table with a few of the elected village fathers. A lone light bulb hung from the ceiling, casting an eerie light upon the furrowed brows of the grave and earnest planners. The town hall was also the jail; in one corner, partitioned by chicken wire, was an iron cot and a tattered mattress. It was unoccupied, attesting to the law abiding as well as sober quality of the citizenry—at least that early in the evening.

The problem was plain and its solution simple. The

wholesale pillaging of Deep Harbor by its junior citizenry in the name of saintly vandalism must be prevented. To do so the principal street and its lone appendage leading down to the water front was to be patrolled by two men. In view of the slimness of the village treasury, the meager sum with which to hire these protectors was to be provided by Hugo, Jacques, and Philo. All of this had the unanimity of the earnest group of civic minded conspirators. The barkeepers whose generosity made this plan feasible found solace in the very great probability that their financial outlay would be well returned by the tranquility of the thirsty and free spending crowd who would celebrate All Saints' Day with an evening of uninhibited and boisterous beer guzzling, free from the consequences of an also uninhibited teen-age vandalism.

There remained only one problem. Where in this remote and isolated village from which the able bodied men had long since departed for purposes of war or profit could two men be found to stand the rigors of a night of patrol duty?

Hugo had half the answer. There was Bullfrog Upton. Upton lived down on his ancient cabin fishing boat moored at the ferry dock and was for the moment without income. Being a commercial fisherman of questionable reliability and sobriety he had recently lost his fishing nets to the sovereign state because of the doubtful legality of both his setting of nets and his keeping of forbidden fish. This was no new experience for Upton; in fact, he gloried in such predicaments and was confident that fortune would one day smile upon him and he would obtain more nets and resume his illegal activities. And at least he still had the means of quenching his thirst, in terms of hard liquor, and his remaining meager requirements could be well taken care of by odd jobs, for instance, the patrolling of Deep Harbor on All Saints' night.

Philo had the other half of the answer. Red Crawford of Big Island was without gainful pursuit at the moment and staying at Hattie's boardinghouse. Red was seldom seen on the mainland, but the pre-season kill of venison, particularly of does and spikeless fawns on Big Island, had attracted the conservation officers. Red's absence from the island might spare him from embarrassing and perhaps incriminating interrogation. Furthermore, it was three weeks before the opening of the legal season, and with the weather unseasonably warm, it would be too early to stock up on antlered deer carcasses in anticipation of the demand of the red coated army of city hunters from *below*. Among this annual pilgrimage of big game seekers from the machines, the offices, and the factories *below*, Red was known as a good provider, particularly for those who would avoid the ruggedness of the hunt in favor of beer drinking, poker playing pastimes. In the interim, Red ate and slept well at Hattie's and might perhaps be useful in lawful pursuits, such as protecting a defenseless village against Halloween pillagers.

And thus Bullfrog Upton and Red Crawford became Deep Harbor's temporary symbols of law and order. The devastation of the mobile properties of the villagers on this annual night of dread and fear had, by the farsightedness and civic consciousness of a handful of barkeepers and village fathers, been guarded against. This year the sun would not rise over a scene of displaced outhouses, crippled jalopies, physical absurdities, and domestic embarrassments, after a night of terror and misgivings.

.   .   .

A harvest moon hung low in the sky as darkness hid the shabbiness of the unkempt village of Deep Harbor. As it swung higher in its orbit the sharp outline of Big Island loomed prominently over the waters of the straits and the shimmering reflection of the moonlight danced as if it too had caught the spirit of the night. Behind the village the dense forest of pine and cedar seemed close and comforting.

Within the motley beer halls, the adult population of Deep Harbor, in an atmosphere reeking of stale beer and tobacco smoke, quaffed its drinks and swung into its nightly fun and frolic. A feeling of security pervaded the carefree mood of the hardy drinkers, while outside the stalwart figures of the village guardians for a night patrolled the street, alert to any act of juvenile destruction.

Determined to perform with firmness and resolve the charge entrusted to them, they had laid their plans well. Upton was to patrol southward from Hugo's beer hall to where the street ended with a lone cabin and the wilderness. Red was to patrol northward to where the street lost itself in the county road and, since this distance was shorter than the other, he was to include the angling roadway to the water front. They were to meet at Hugo's building, compare notes, and then for the sake of variety, exchange patrol areas.

The night wore on. Through the murky windows of Hugo's tavern these trusty guardians of peace noted the thinning of the crowd. Soon the last bleary drinker staggered homeward, lights were turned off, and only the moon, now high in the starlit sky, afforded comforting light. The village folks slumbered, peacefully and soundly. Upon meeting again at the darkened beer hall, the patrollers compared notes. Neither had seen any stray juvenile bent on mischief or any misplaced object.

They continued the conscientious prosecution of their duties. Meeting again and feeling weary they sat for a

while, smoking and commenting on the exemplary peace-
fulness of the village, and then they departed upon their
wearisome and uneventful rounds.

Later they once more sat for smokes and rest, remarking upon the beauty of the moonlight over the waters and
the distant islands. Upton pulled from his shabby sweater a
bottle that gleamed invitingly in the moonlight, pulled the
cork, and proffered Red a drink. After taking a deep
draught, Red returned the bottle and Upton took his turn,
whereupon they resumed their duties.

The patrol distances seemed to shorten. The meetings
became more frequent and the time between remarkably
brief, and, of course, the bottle emptied quickly. Red meanwhile found another in the recesses of his voluminous coat
and the commentary on the virtues of Deep Harbor's teen-
agers and the beauty of the moon bathed islands gave way
to reminiscence of their youth including, of course, their
Halloween depredations.

They remarked about how times had changed. With
all of these inviting privies the youth of today just didn't
seem to have the spirit of wholesome, if perhaps destructive, fun. No indeed, a healthy youngster worth his keep
would certainly desert the warmth and comfort of home on
a night like this to indulge in a little innocent prankishness.
These modern youths just didn't have the gumption to assert their rights to a little pillaging on a night set aside for
just that purpose. Warmed by the fiery liquor, Red and Upton soon drifted into boasting of their own youthful prowess in vandalism.

By now they were patrolling their areas together. Soon
tiring of the weary trudging, they found that by taking their
position in the rear of Hugo's beer hall they could view the

street in either direction, including the angling water front appendage.

As they sat enjoying the close intimacy of gossip, boasting, and reminiscence, the moon cleared the ragged façade of the crude building to light up the two unassuming privies which served Hugo's beer hall. Whether it was the effect of the moonlight, the liquor, or just a return to childish impishness, they mused awhile upon Hugo's attempt at identification. On the left privy was a crudely lettered sign, now prominent in the silver light, proclaiming it to be for "Sitters"; on the other a similar identification indicated that it was for "Standers." As if of the same mind they both rose and interchanged the signs. Then they resumed their patrolling in earnest, weaving perhaps a little uncertainly, until they came to the forest fringe. There they paused to take another drink and then headed to the other limit.

Reaching the place where the street ended in the lonely county road, they drank again and with visible stagger returned to the rear of the beer hall. Here they sat and in high good humor contemplated the consequences of the misplaced identification signs. It was, they both agreed, the dullest Halloween they had ever experienced, whereupon they argued long and loudly about the technique of upsetting a privy. As if to break the monotony of the night, they both concluded that a demonstration was in order and thereupon proceeded down the angling water front road until they came to Hattie's boardinghouse. There loomed Hattie's especially inviting outhouse. Red, with rare skill and speed, upset it neatly; Upton meanwhile demonstrated his own skill by placing another on top of the woodshed. They then turned back to their favorite rendezvous, and

by the time they had reached Hugo's, every privy enroute
spoke eloquently of their skill and artistry.

Then, as if to lend flavor to their handiwork, they returned to carry a particularly dilapidated and mobile outhouse and place it neatly before the post office door. Tired
by their exertions and feeling the need for further rest and
refreshment, the village guardians turned toward their rest-
ing spot, but blurred vision and an intervening fence mis-
led their footsteps and in the apparent myriad of trees and
posts and buildings they found themselves in unfamiliar
surroundings. Defeated in their efforts to find their proper
bearings, they dropped wearily to rest beside a huge cylin-
drical oil tank which by its props and shoring was evidently
awaiting permanent installation.

They sat for a time looking down the gentle slope toward the water front and at the glistening moonlight on the
straits against the backdrop of Big Island looming dark and
large against the starlit sky. But it was late October, and the
night was frosty. Although well fortified within with warming liquor, outwardly they were cold. Red responded to the
chilling force by rising to stamp his feet and swing his arms
vigorously to stimulate circulation. Conversation was lag-
ging, the boasting having spent itself in idle contemplation
and lamentation over a Halloween night completely wasted.

Red thought of his comfortable attic cot at Hattie's
boardinghouse and gazed wistfully down the slope where
the moon lighted the whitewashed fence surrounding the
premises. Upton thought of the warmth of his bunk in the
tiny craft that was his home.

One more pass of the bottle and its comforting influence was spent. Staggering and weaving ludicrously, Red
swung the empty bottle crashing against the side of the
huge oil tank, showering the now reclining Upton with

splintered glass. Upton staggered groggily to his feet and swung furiously at Red, missed, and both went down in a tangled, drunken heap.

Soon exhausted by unaccustomed exertion, they extricated themselves from their belligerent embrace and sat groggily on the cold ground, staring at the glistening dampened spot where Red's bottle had splintered against the metal tank. Was this the answer to a night of boredom? Was here the opportunity to execute a prank that forever would preclude the boasting of even the greatest of all pranksters?

As if of one mind, they staggered to their feet. With a mighty kick, Upton loosened a supporting wedge while Red deftly slid another from its sill. The great tank moved slowly at first and then, with unrealistic acceleration, sped down the slope. With hardly a pause it splintered Hattie's whitewashed fence and crashed with a rending screech through the tiny chicken barn. Amid flying wood and feathers it continued swiftly on its destructive way, clipping trees and fences, to end with a resounding, booming splash into the waters of the strait.

.   .   .

Captain John Wadsworth of the huge ore carrier *Iron Maiden* was bringing his ship through the tortuous inner channel of the straits. The moonlight reflected on the white foam of the bow swell and danced on the crest of the angling wake. Outside the pilot house, the deck watch paced to and fro, glancing frequently at his watch and chafing under the monotonous, useless vigil of his endless chore. The ship's bell had just clanged the hour of two. Another hour and he would be relieved to join the crap game in the companionway of the deserted galley at the after end.

He stared pensively into the brilliant sheen of the waning moon reflected on the water. Suddenly the blunt snout of an unusual object bobbed within his vision to submerge quickly and appear again. With a frightened cry he sounded the alarm and pointed hysterically at the strange and sinister creature. The Captain stepped quickly to the port side observation bridge in time to see a strange, dark craft, round and of great length, pitch high into the swell of the swiftly moving ship, then deeply into the turbulent trough of the ship's wheel wash. Five paces brought him to the pilot house where, with the instinctive resolve of his calling, he dialed the ship to shore channel of the radio phone.

.   .   .

Wartime called for extraordinary vigilance of home defense. In consequence, the forces of the National Coast Guard were well deployed in the vulnerable and strategic areas of lake commerce. Not the least of these was the important link of the Great Upper Lake to the lower industrial areas by the intricate canal system of locks and water lifts. Here a powerful detachment of the Coast Guard was firmly intrenched to protect the flow of vital ore and minerals to the munition manufacturing areas *below*.

Lieutenant Commander Alfred Frick was on watch. He sat at his desk in the tiny cubicle that was his office. For the fourth time that night he read the confidential manual entitled "Strategic Defense of the Interlake Canal Area" and pondered the possibility of attack by long range aircraft or by infiltration of enemy saboteurs to disrupt lake commerce, as the manual so patiently explained.

The low burble of the radio phone aroused him from his reverie. He lifted the receiver to hear the crisp metallic voice of Captain Wadsworth calling Interlake station by code. Frick responded mechanically in kind. Methodically he recorded the coded message on his report pad. The conversation completed, he signed off on his channel and reached for his code book to decipher the message. Slowly the message took shape and meaning. After completion and checking, he leaned back to read the now intelligible dispatch with understanding:

Steamer *Iron Maiden* downbound channel off Deep Harbor—strange, unlighted watercraft, mostly submerged, approached port side, missed bow and washed off course by wake—estimated length fifty feet—round deck—no apparent upside armament.

Stunned for the moment by the portentous implication of the message, Frick searched his mind frantically for the indicated course of action. The manual stated that clearly; it read:

If attack should come on the Great Lakes Coastal waters the enemy would be operating from both land and sea. The nearest military post headquarters should be notified. In the event that organized State Constabulary is immediately available, the mobility of such civilian police forces should be at once enlisted.

Swiftly he sprang into action and summoned his orderlies. A call placed him in touch with the Fifth Anti-aircraft Regimental Headquarters located above the Interlake Canal. Then he startled the long distance operator by placing an A-1 priority call for the State Police Headquarters in Straits City. Having complied thus far with the explicit instructions of the manual he scanned the lake charts. Deep Harbor was three hours distant by fast picket boats and five by the slower but more effective cutters. Outside, the detachment was racing into formation by orders of the quickly responding petty officers, and the Commandant arrived in full action regalia in an unobtrusive but exceedingly useful jeep.

Fifty miles distant from Deep Harbor, Sergeant Andrews and Corporal Korsky of the State Police were cruising along the unkempt, forest lined secondary road system. They flashed their spotlight from side to side, alert to detect rural pranksters or other revellers of the occasion, the while watchful for pre-season deer poachers and other petty law violators. On a hilltop overlooking a lake studded area bathed in bright moonlight, they paused to take in the scenic view as well as to better locate the illegal shining of deer.

Over their patrol radio came a call for the attention of all cars, followed by an astounding directive to converge upon and establish a road block at a coded intersection, there to await further instruction. As Korsky quickly accelerated the police car, Andrews thumbed through his code book to locate the mysterious rendezvous. It was a few miles from the village of Deep Harbor. A call to Deep Harbor was no new experience. Street brawls, car collisions, and petty thievery occurred frequently in that policeless settlement and the arresting powers of the State Constabulary were frequently needed. This, however, was a call seldom broadcast short of riot and catastrophe. The implication of the general order called for speed; with red head and tail flashers the vehicle roared over precarious, rutted roadways in response.

From the recently rejuvenated though still ancient Fort Superior where the Fifth A.A. Regiment headquartered, two trucks laden with fully armed infantry roared through the guarded gates, startling the slumbering Interlake City. After a few miles they left the smooth concrete to careen wildly and at desperate speed through swamp roads, around unbanked curves, and through narrow bridges in the direction of Deep Harbor.

. . .

Since the day of infamy which this narrative seeks to record, Deep Harbor has returned to the serenity of its lonely North Woods existence. However, the eastern sky had only a suggestion of light to cast upon the absurdity of the never to be forgotten scene on that fateful morning after a night of Halloween revelry.

Out on the waters of the straits played the searchlights of uncounted picket boats, darting to and fro in a broad sweeping encirclement of the water front area. From Hugo's beer hall to Philo's bar and on down to the Catholic mission glistened the fixed bayonets of the deployed infantry. On the angling roadway leading to the water's edge stood a solid bristling phalanx of armed police cruisers, the insignia of their protective calling emblazoned by their red flashing emergency lights.

Nestled in questionable comfort in the debris that had been Hattie's chicken barn were the prostrate forms of the faithful village guardians, peacefully asleep, dreaming no doubt with delightful satisfaction of a night's work and a magnificent accomplishment.

Around them stood a threatening, angry circle of bristling uniforms and milling, irate townsmen. Police Sergeant Andrews looked first at Philo, then at Hugo, and finally at Jacques. It had been, they all agreed, a hell of a night.

FOREST TRAILS

In the plush dignity of a resplendent office in a towering skyscraper that dominated the skyline of a bustling city down lake, six men constituting the board of strategy of a mining enterprise sat in consultation. From the window the blue of the lake framed two long breakwaters wide apart at the shore line and converging to a narrow opening far out in the deep waters of the open lake. Smoke belched from the tiny, busy tugs as they chugged within the protective area, assisting the giant ore carriers arriving from the distant mystery of the land *above below*, their smokestack ensigns gleaming proudly in the autumn sun.

The subject that commanded the earnest attention of the group had far reaching implications, implications that would touch the lives and comforts of people in remote places, that would lay a beneficial hand upon the giant commerce of the Great Lakes waterways, that would shuffle for better or for worse the both delicate and sensitive economy of the pulsating manufacturing centers in the urban areas *below*.

On a densely wooded island far up in the North Country where the arteries of lake commerce spun a web of intricate patterns in the dark loneliness of vast forested spaces, was an outcrop of ore indicating an extensive deposit. Its presence there in the tangle of swamps and woods and waters was no secret to the inquisitive geologists nor to the trappers, hunters, and fishermen who roamed the area. Nor was it any secret to the farsighted men of enterprise whose task it was to provide the raw materials that fed the hungry mouths of the diverse and intricate mechanical monsters from whose digestive processes came the goods necessary to an ever demanding industrial civilization. No, what had permitted this ore deposit to retain its primeval and geological concealment was not ignorance of its presence, but the fact that, while it had peculiar chemical and physical properties which made an interesting and complex arrangement of symbols, it had no other value. That is, not until this earnest group of men deigned it a worthy subject for their deliberations.

The chairman voiced the conclusion of the group: the ore deposit was to be sampled carefully and in utmost secrecy. Two of the men present were to visit the area and obtain samples in a manner that would excite neither curiosity nor speculation on the part of the local populace. One of the two who had been selected for the mission was Matthews, who half a dozen years before had spent some time in the area and hence was familiar with the means and manner of its ingress. The other, an engineer named Bradford, was to view the technical and engineering aspects of development and the fidelity of sampling. The former welcomed the opportunity afforded by this mission to escape, if only temporarily, the confining inactivity of desk work; that the mission might require physical exertion beyond the capacity of muscles long grown soft from sedentary habits, did not occur to him. Bradford, accustomed to outdoor activity and energetic action, welcomed the opportunity to explore new country and to dream new conquests; but it failed to occur to him that forest trails and landmarks in retrospect might be stamped indelibly in the mind of his associate in this venture and yet be erased by the obliterating hand of nature.

·   ·   ·

It is a far cry from a carpeted and air conditioned office to the water front of Deep Harbor, where Matthews and Bradford arrived early in the morning a few days later. They had spent the previous night in a small hotel in the frontier atmosphere of Straits City and there had planned the strategy of accomplishing their mission. The ore deposit could be reached by a water landing on a point of the island just south and only a mile distant from it. However, two strangers seeking to hire a power launch might excite the curiosity and speculation which they were seeking to avoid. The alternative, as Matthews had outlined it, was to cross the strait on the tiny ferry and drive east on the island road a matter of half a dozen miles to where an old lumbering road led southward a scant mile. This would place them within three miles of the ore deposit. From the point where the lumber road ended, numerous trails led into the area adjacent to the deposit. Matthews had neglected to add that, except for trail travel, the area was a jungle of tall, wind swept timber and fallen logs with a thick undergrowth of cedar, tamarack, and spruce.

Samples could be obtained and the three mile round trip covered on foot in a matter of three or four hours. Then too, the samples could be carried to the car without anyone being the wiser, whereas certainly such samples carried to a waiting launch would in a matter of hours become the topic of conversation all over Deep Harbor and Big Island as well. Bradford had agreed, but had questioned whether the lumber road was passable by car. Matthews had said that it was, the last time he had traveled it, and the fact that it was still shown on the most recent road maps was an indication that it remained so.

Bradford had next raised the question of identifying the proper trail from the maze of paths that led from the wagon road terminal. "Miss it hell, man, I know that country with my eyes shut," had been Matthews' reply, "we'll get up at daybreak and high tail it for Deep Harbor, have breakfast there, then catch the first ferry trip to the island and we can get our samples and be back to the mainland by noon."

Bradford had nodded assent; it sounded good.

Now, as they sat in their car awaiting the early morning ferry, they reviewed their plans and studied their map again. On one point they had already gone amiss. Deep Harbor had no eating places, and they faced the prospect of a six mile hike on empty stomachs. It was a beautiful though frosty autumn day, and quite by accident their arrival coincided with the last day of November, which was also the last day of deer season. They were reminded of this fact by the red coated passengers who drove off the ferry as she made her first trip to the mainland.

The island bound trip was immediate, and they were the only passengers. As they boarded the little vessel, Corky, the deck hand, noticed first that their car carried a foreign license, that they wore business clothes, and that no hunters' paraphernalia was piled on the back seat. As he entered the tiny pilot house he winked knowingly at the skipper, saying, "Where would them guys be goin'—they ain't hunters, they ain't no fishermen, and what the hell else would anybody come to the island for?"

Leaving the ferry, Bradford and Matthews travelled in high spirits the rough six mile stretch of island road. The lumber road was still there and apparently passable. Halfway to its terminus they were blocked by a fallen tree. A half hour of back breaking labor cleared it, and as Matthews paused to catch his breath he said, "Should of brought an axe."

After a few more road blocks of fortunately smaller trees, they reached the end of the road trail, where they turned the car around so that it was headed back. This took quite a while, for apparently the builder of this road had not anticipated the need of accommodating four wheeled vehicles, and nature had further encroached upon its restricted right of way. Bradford noted the several foot trails radiating from the end of the roadway. He noted also an inch or more of snow cover which the still strong rays of a November sun had failed to melt through the protective cover of dense tree growth. He glanced at his watch. It was nine. "Could do with a cup of coffee," he said.

Meanwhile, Matthews studied the trails and confidently announced, "Let's go, this is it—be there in less than an hour," and he led the way.

For a while they followed it single file, Matthews leading. Finding cross trails and departures and conflicting deer

runways, he studied each briefly and proceeded with a
cheerful "this is it." After a few twists and turns, with
Bradford marvelling at Matthews' remarkable memory and
prowess in the woods, they came to a wagon road. Less than
a hundred feet away stood their car. Bradford looked at his
watch and saw that it was nine-thirty. Both men laughed.
"Shucks," exclaimed Matthews, "I should have known that
the left center trail is the one we should take. Come on,
let's go."

At the end of an hour, their pace considerably slowed
by fatigue and trails cluttered with fallen trees, they came
to a small tamarack swamp; here the trail lost itself in an
obscurity of bog and morass. Puzzled, Matthews said,
"Don't remember this at all—must have got off on one of
those damned deer runways." Then, squinting at the sun,
he added, "That's south there—we should be going halfway
between south and west."

Carefully skirting the swamp they ran across several
trails, but these were indistinguishable from deer runways.
They chose one at random, and after following its tortuous
meander for half an hour, they came upon a small clearing.
Through the trees they could see the shimmer of open water. Emerging from the thicket, they looked out over a large
cove to a nearby island and remarked about the beauty of
its setting. They followed the shore line of the cove a few
hundred feet to where an outcropping of the rock formed
a barrier to their progress. "Hell," exclaimed Matthews, "I
know right where we're at now—let me take that map a minute and I'll show you."

Spreading the map on a flat rock, Matthews indicated
the cove with his pencil and then drew a line leading to the
ore deposit. "All we got to do is strike due west about a
mile, see?" he explained. Then he continued with, "This

outcrop follows a ridge back all the way—remember trailing a wounded deer here one time and it brought me right to the ore."

"Is there a trail on the ridge?" asked Bradford.

"Shucks, don't need one—can't lose me now," Matthews replied.

Bradford studied the map. "Looks okay on the map, but if you aren't sure, safest bet is for us to follow the shore line to this point here." He indicated it on the map, saying, "That'll put us just a mile away from where we're headed and on such a narrow neck of land we couldn't get off trail far enough to miss."

"We'd just be walking four miles to make one," snapped Matthews and he led the way.

Five minutes of following the pathless ridge, stumbling over boulders and climbing over fallen trees brought them to a halt for rest. "Boy, I remember this spot like it was yesterday—sighted the wounded buck right here and took another shot at him," exclaimed Matthews. "Betcha if I had time to look I'd find an empty shell. It's not far now, let's go."

In another half hour they came unexpectedly to a cliff. They skirted it, detouring the many fallen trees, stumbling over huge rounded boulders, and snagging their clothes on the tangled, brittle branches. After an hour of this, Matthews sank exhausted on a log seat. "Cripes," he exclaimed, "we should be there now—wonder if we aren't too far south."

Bradford sat down and lit his pipe, saying, "Should of brought lunch—got wrinkles in my belly." This brought no response from Matthews, who had started to remove his shoes. "Stop it," shouted Bradford, seeing the swollen ankles, "you won't get 'em back on if you do that!" Matthews obeyed, and anxiety showed plainly on his now flushed countenance.

Bradford looked at his watch. It was two. Looking toward the sun, he noticed that it was overcast. "There goes our direction finder," he muttered, "should have brought a compass."

He then fell to studying the map. If Matthews had correctly recognized the cove as being the one on the map, then logic would suggest returning to the cove in order to place themselves in a position of known location. Then, by staying on the coast line, they would reach their starting point. Following the shore line to the left might bring them back to the island road. This would mean, however, following inlets and indentations and perhaps impassable swamps of dense cedar and tamarack. It would also mean giving up the object of their mission. Following the shore line to the right would bring them, eventually, to the point of land near the ore body. From there an equally long, but more definite, shore line would bring them back to the ferry dock. With the best of luck, neither way could be accomplished in the remaining hours of daylight. Any attempt to reach the car by a direct overland route would be foolhardy in the absence of a definite trail and without the benefit of a compass. Furthermore, should darkness overtake them, fallen trees and treacherous boulders might trip them into serious injury.

"Look here, Matthews," commanded Bradford, "how sure are you that we're near the ore body?"

Matthews asserted feebly that he was certain that it was near at hand, if only they continued in the westerly direction.

"Then let's go," Bradford said, "if you can make it."

The feeble sunlight was a poor substitute for a compass. Traveling in the direction of the brightest overcast would at that hour be westward. Through dense thickets of cedar, ice coated tamarack swamps, and groves of towering spruce and pine they stumbled, hopeful that the next log fall they so painfully climbed or the next jagged cliff over which they crawled would reveal the friendly aspects of a known location. Matthews' condition now required frequent rests which only served to make the resumption of their weary wandering a tortuous nightmare. Always there were tantalizing trails and runways tempting departure from the certainty of direction. Hours later they emerged from a tangled overgrown fire slash to come with startling suddenness upon a rock promontory tapering off in a long sharp tongue of land to a rocky, boulder strewn vanishing point in the clear waters of the open lake.

There Matthews, his ankles swollen grotesquely, his face contorted from pain, dropped on the hard rock surface, buried his head in his arms, and sobbed convulsively.

Bradford, taking the map, studied his bearings in an attempt to identify this obvious landmark. It was without doubt the point of land directly south of the ore deposit. Coaxing Matthews to a kindlier bed of ground balsam and admonishing him to remain where he was, Bradford headed rapidly northward.

Guided by shimmering waters first to his left, then to his right, he stumbled half an hour later upon the ore outcrop. Swiftly he broke ore specimen from the bedding planes, carefully noting their relative position. After sketching the physical characteristics and the lay of the land in his notebook, he shouldered his sack of samples and retraced his steps to the point of land. Matthews sat where he had left him, disconsolate, whimpering in obvious pain.

Noting that Matthews had removed his shoes, Bradford cursed softly. Matthews was done for and there remained the problem of bringing him to safety. He looked at the swollen, shapeless ankles and the grotesquely deformed feet. Walking the stony beach, climbing the craggy boulders and cliffs, and the moss covered ledges of forest trails was an ordeal even with the benefit of sturdy woodsman's boots, let alone in stockinged feet. And night was rapidly descending.

In the fading light Bradford studied the map. With a small forked twig he stepped off the scale, following the tortuous coast line. It was five miles to the ferry landing, five miles of stony, pathless beach. It would then be six miles to the lumber road and another mile to where the car had been left at the wagon road terminus. At best it would require four hours. Taking stock of the situation, he considered the factors: the temperature was far below freezing and, even now, but a faint light lay low on the western horizon. Bradford noted with satisfaction, however, that the overcast was receding and that there might be moonlight. He could reach the car and make the last ferry to the mainland. There, with good luck, he might find someone with a small power boat who could make the eight mile run to the point of land to pick up Matthews.

Difficult problems once faced with definite action soon lose their formidability, and they are not always solved in the elegance of skyscraper offices or by boards of strategy. Bradford moved speedily to the task before him. He kindled a fire and placed a huge stock of firewood within Matthews' reach. The hysterical fright on his companion's face alarmed him. Sternly he admonished him to remain where he was and to keep the fire burning.

Turning to start up the beach, Bradford saw his samples. For a moment he hesitated, then reaching for the bag he shouldered it and stepped briskly on his way.

Boulder strewn shore lines were not made for pedestrian travel. Neither were forests, whose twisted, unused trails are lost in tangled undergrowth and fallen trees. In the faded uncertainty of moonlight, reflecting deceiving smoothness under foot, Bradford finally came to the Island road. Relieved of the torture of jagged footholds, he hurried confidently up the road, its gravelled surface a grateful assurance to his tired feet.

Two hours later he turned down the lumber road, elated by the knowledge that this would be the last long mile. The moon, now high, cast weird patterns on the slight snow cover, a crazy contrast of white patchwork surrounding fanciful moats and abysses of shadowy treachery and hazard. Invisible branches stung with merciless impudence, and in the frosty air the snapping of twigs sounded in frightening exaggeration. White patches gleamed, took shape, and glided in retreat as snowshoe hares awakened to flee the unaccustomed trespass. When Bradford at last stumbled against the car and tossed the samples behind the seat, he reflected upon the wisdom of having turned it in its outgoing direction. Sinking heavily into the cushioned seat he said aloud, "That's the only thing we did right all day."

.   .   .

The small craft rounded the moonlit, choppy waters lying off the point and proceeded cautiously to work its way through the rocky shoal. Bradford watched apprehensively for the firelight which would locate Matthews. After probing the shore line for a safe landing, the boatman threw a searchlight in a sweeping arc against the background of thick, dark forest. It stopped at a wispy pillar of gray smoke rising straight until it cleared the protective lee of the tree line and mushroomed into vague and eerie dissipation.

They carried Matthews, protesting in painful sobs, to the little craft and were soon cutting through moonlit spray in the direction of Deep Harbor.

The boatman helped the stricken man into the car. Bradford reflected a moment upon the day's events and thought of the ore specimen safely stowed away. "Mission completed," he said to himself, and then added, "in utmost secrecy, too."

Gratefully the boatman acknowledged the fee and the handsome tip Bradford bestowed upon him. Turning as if to go, he hesitated and then returned to the car. "Say Mister," he said to Bradford, "are you the same guys what went over on the ferry this morning to git samples?"

ICE BRIDGE

It looked easy. There in the far distance loomed the sharp outlines of the Canadian headlands, purple against the dazzling white of the seemingly endless snow. Nearer, the wooded areas marked unmistakably the myriad of islands on the frozen bosom of Island Bay. To the left was Moose Island, while straight ahead lay tiny Juniper and behind it Bass Island, Birch, Corbett, and Rabbit Back. On the right stretched the spiny back of Gull Reef, almost but not quite touching the northernmost bluffs of Big Island. It was just as the map showed it to be.

Bowen folded the map and turned to Benson and Freeman. "How about it, fellows? Want to try it?"

Bowen and Benson had been in the Island Bay area before. But their visits here, in pursuit of their geological and technical investigations, had been made in the delightful atmosphere of summer and in the comfort of sturdy and reliable watercraft. Now, however, the heavy ice bridge locked the islands to the mainland in a silent embrace, and only when necessity compelled did travellers brave the icy surface to pursue their errands.

Sitting in the comfortable warmth of their car at the foot of the water front road, they saw the smooth ice stretching endlessly across the strait toward distant horizons. The panorama of islands pointed the way. Rutted wheel tracks led from the road over and through the shore snow to lose themselves in the glaze of the smooth, bare ice. The winter sun that morning shone from a cloudless sky to belie the bitter cold that held the Northland in its icy grip.

Inquiry had disclosed that cars had been travelling quite often between the mainland and the lumber cove on the north side of Big Island. Was the ice safe for automobile travel? Certainly. The mail truck hadn't missed but one trip the past month, and a truck load of baled hay had gone over this very morning. Yes, there were shoal spots where the water currents held the ice to an unsafe thickness, and the backwash swells of the open lake below had broken great cracks in the channel area now concealed by treacherous skim ice and new fallen snow. Just stay away from those places by following the longer route through the islands and you can't go wrong. Watch for the cedar boughs stuck into holes in the ice.

It had sounded easy then and it looked even easier now. Bowen let the clutch in and moved slowly through the rutted and crusted shore snow. In a few hundred feet the tire chains bit into the hard smooth ice with a ringing crunch. Straight ahead was Juniper Island, and in the clear atmosphere the cedar boughs, though far apart, gave them comforting assurance. Bowen picked up speed; Benson and Freeman settled back in their seats relaxed and confident. It was just like travelling on a multi-lane super highway.

In winter, travel between Big Island and the mainland is always an unpredictable possibility. When winters are extremely cold, as they usually are, the thick ice bridge offers safe transportation for those who know the way. When storms on the big open lake below lash with relentless fury, as they often do, the swell of the tumultuous sea quickens the current of the strait to cause great cracks stretching many miles up into Island Bay. Then the quiet that follows, abetted by the intense cold, seals the open areas with thin new ice with treacherous and deceiving perfection.

If, however, winters are mild or interrupted by frequent thaws, or by chance the protective snows lie heavy on the icy surface, or warm south winds whip the great ice fields into unyielding movement, then Big Island bows gracefully to enforced isolation. It is said among the islanders that no matter what the ice condition may be, if there be need for travel to the mainland and that need be sufficiently compelling, some means to do so can always be found. To this the timid add the need for miracle and prayer.

Bowen passed the first cedar marker, sighted the next quickly, and the vehicle carrying the three men sped swiftly and uneventfully toward Juniper Island. The marked route then turned and twisted for no apparent reason from island to island and finally, as if to end the sublimity of its travel excellence, it ended in a maze of conflicting rutted tracks in the lee of Corbett Island. Reference to the map indicated that the lumber cove lay directly south and so it did, for the pilings of the ragged wharf protruded hideously through the clean white blanket of drifted snow and were visible even at that great distance.

Just an hour from the mainland brought them to the rocky beach of the lumber cove. A few rough lurches, and the heavy car stood on the solid, inviting island road from which the snow had been neatly plowed. Not bad, they all agreed, while inwardly they felt, but would not admit, a satisfying and comforting relief. But they had business to attend to, business compelling enough to risk the hazards of thirty miles of silent, icy waste, and then to return again to the comforting though primitive trappings of the mainland.

The sun was still two hours above nightfall when the three men returned to the beach head on the cove. Picking their way carefully around the protruding boulders, they reached the smooth ice to feel again the exhilaration of the unimpeded and wide travel lanes that led to Corbett Island. In the lee of that island, where the rutted tracks branched in meaningless directions, they paused to check their bearings. To the west the sky was clear and the lowering sun outlined the island chain and the twisting line of cedar boughs in crystal clarity.

What they failed to observe, however, was the almost imperceptible change in atmosphere. Corbett Island and Rabbit Back concealed the north and east horizons, else they might have noted the obscurity of the headlands in that direction. The frosty bite of the morning's bitter cold had given way to an icy, penetrating chill. A gentle northeast breeze prevailed.

Bowen swung the car to the left and picked out the cedar marker ahead. In less than a mile he sighted the second marker that signified the tortuous circuit around Birch Island, and then the straightaway to the mainland. The first warning came as a wisp of snow momentarily obscured their vision and then cleared again.

Barely a thousand feet away the cedar bough near Birch Island showed sharp and clear. Once this marker had been reached the long miles to the mainland were without turnings. Bowen picked up speed. From the northeast great dark clouds reared above the islands. The setting sun still shone bright in a clear western sky.

Then a few flakes fell and the sky above took on a

steely gray. Like a misty curtain dropping with incredible speed, Birch Island and the cedar marker disappeared in soft white obscurity and the blizzard struck.

Bowen held the car on course, driving dead ahead in the vain hope that a clearing moment might assure him of his direction. Long after he should have reached the marker or the island, he drove through the confusing swirl of streaky white, while the gusts of wind now howled with ominous insistence and the car shook as it pitched through the drifted snow banks.

With uncertainty came hesitancy. Bowen slowed as if the slackening speed would by some miracle restore a sense of direction or give a moment of visibility. Instead the car plowed into a white blanket that had neither shape nor apparent substance, to shudder to a stop. Hopefully he backed up to make a run for the heavy, invisible drift ahead. The chains rasped loudly while the drift climbed fender high to lock the car in unyielding grasp. A gurgle of water and a sickening list of the left rear tire told the worst. In that world of white, in that vastness of frozen waste and solid ice, the car had found the softness of a shoal spot. With all the scientific splendor of its power and the magnificent comfort of its mobility, and its responsiveness to the will of the human mind, the car sank in ignominious defeat and helplessness, a victim of the villainous caprice of nature.

The men stepped out into the cruel blast of the tempest and the cutting sting of flying snow to take stock of their situation. These three had faced problems before, problems of commerce, of engineering, of chemistry, of human equations, of giant structures, of complex mechanical processes, and of intricate, illusive physics. But in this vastness of white there were no slide rules, no test tubes, no tables of physical factors, formulae, or equations. There were no stars and no sun, no place of beginning—not even the comfort of a pocket compass. There was only the swiftly approaching darkness and the limitless empty space, the unrelenting blast of a pitiless hurricane, the bitterness of intense cold, and the consciousness of peril.

With reluctance they abandoned their personal belongings. The ordeal before them would be harsh and grave enough without the burden of material possessions. In the lee of their partially submerged vehicle, they weighed the factors in their favor. Freeman had taken note of the first indicated direction of the wind when they had left the safety of the lumber cove travelling in a northerly direction. In the fast fading light, their coats shielding the map, they studied the course. Walking with the wind would take them south of their mainland destination. A quarter to the north would be nearly correct, that is, providing that the assumed wind direction was exactly northeast. This, then, was their only constant, crudely assumed perhaps but nevertheless indicative. Benson noted with grim humor that at least they were favored by having the wind behind them.

A last cigarette, a last look at their hapless vehicle, and they were on their way, travelling abreast. The wind's roar drowned all attempted conversation. Light enough remained to see their footing, but long before they would reach the safety of their mainland destination, darkness would conceal the hazardous ice on which they walked.

When they stumbled at last on the rocky shore of the first island, they huddled in the friendly shelter of its dense tree growth. A lone coyote glided shadowlike in apparent resentment to human intrusion, but the incident aroused little interest in the increasing consciousness of their personal peril. Freeman suggested a change in formation. Travelling abreast gave no control of constant direction; he suggested instead that they go single file with the rear man controlling direction. This they tried and found effective, but closing darkness defeated its purpose. Freeman stayed in the rear. So long as he felt the sting of flying snow on his thinly protected right ear, he knew he was holding the course. A huddled consultation suggested chanting as they walked. So in single file they again proceeded, chanting with the monotony of repetition, "Bowen, Benson, Freeman, Bowen, Benson, Freeman, Bowen . . ."

Again and again this chanting rose in sharp contrast to the moaning of the relentless wind as they walked stiff leggedly over the bare slippery ice or stumbled painfully through deep drifts in the blackness before them. Freeman, noting Bowen's chant out of Benson's line of march would shout a directional correction. Grim as the situation was, they could not help but see the drollery of the arrangement. Several times they fell on the slippery surface or stumbled through invisible drifts. Fatigue pursued them, inviting rest. But all three knew that rest would be a victory for the elements which sought to destroy them. Hour after hour they pressed on, the chanting at times breaking into weird hoarseness or rising in painful sobs. Merciful numbness relieved them of the penetrating cold, while their breathing became difficult and their nostrils and eyebrows gathered icy coating.

There was blackness, impenetrable blackness; space, illimitable space; treachery underfoot, weird wailing above, and unmerciful lashing from behind, a villainy compounded by nature seeking to destroy. In answer, chilled voices chanted, "Bowen, Benson, Freeman,—Bowen, Benson, Freeman,—Bowen . . ."

Hours later it was Bowen who first stumbled on the round rocks of a beach, and with a shout the others joined him. Here was land, but what land? Huddled together to grasp respite from overwhelming weariness they rested. Freeman spoke, "Listen."

There was a strange silence. Turning toward the lowering wind no stinging snow whipped their faces. Slowly a weird faint light lent shape and ghostly reality to them and to the huge rocks of the beach. They stood a few moments in wonderment, while dawn came from the east to disclose faintly the whiteness of the land. A few hundred feet to the south was the foot of the water front road, now shrouded in giant drifts. Freeman's face wore a triumphant smile as he looked over the strait to the scene of their weary ordeal. Benson with a grin turned toward him. "Hell, man, what are you looking so damned smug about—you missed it by two hundred feet."

HATTIE'S BOARDINGHOUSE

HATTIE PAYNER and Eli Wallenon had three things in common: both had been bereaved of their respective spouses; both were opportunists cashing in on the primal needs of the water front village of Deep Harbor; and each nurtured an antipathy toward the other that bordered on the ridiculous.

Here, if in need of the comforting encouragement of spiritual communion, one could find it in the two struggling churches at either end of Deep Harbor's single thoroughfare. If one needed relief from the discomfort of a parched and dusty throat, it could be found in the tiny spring which flowed from the hillside at the edge of the village. If, however, the compelling pangs of hunger created illusory images of ham and eggs and steaming coffee, and the dust and grime and sweat of weary travel cried out for the cleansing balm of soap and water, such needs could find solace only in the sardines and questionable crackers of the local general store and in the chilling waters of the lake front.

Deep Harbor had no eating establishments. Having few visitors from outside, such facilities were perhaps not important. It also had no waterworks, and the high cost of drilling wells through the hard core of the limestone ridge below was beyond the financial means of the impoverished villagers. In consequence, the few travellers who visited or passed through Deep Harbor either remained hungry or ate at the grocery counter, while the folk who lived there depended upon rain barrels, the hillside spring, or the lake front for their water needs.

Occasionally however, the need for prepared food for transient workers became urgent, for example when the Highway Department began driving through a connecting roadway. Then one year there was a lingering drought when the rain barrels yawned dry and empty, and carrying buckets of water up the steep slope from the water front became unbearably arduous. The opportunities revealed by these needs found response in the enterprising natures of Hattie Payner and Eli Wallenon.

Hattie's husband had left her a small but substantial frame house on the angling roadway to the water front. He had also left her a chicken barn with a whitewashed fence surrounding it, a woodshed, an imposing privy, and a dozen or so laying hens. As Social Security, old age assistance, and publicly financed widows' pensions were as yet below the political horizon, Hattie's needs went beyond the income producing capacity of these material possessions.

Eli's wife left him half a dozen unruly rough and tumble offspring, but not much else. His prowess with the axe could obtain for him employment in the woods, but such opportunities were in the distant logging camps. His paternal disciplinary powers were needed at home, else this motherless brood might play with matches, swallow the family cutlery, or let the fire go out. On the other hand, the six growing youngsters had a great capacity for food, a capacity far beyond that afforded by any income that might be derived from uncertain local employment.

When contractor McCarthy from *Below* found it necessary to obtain board for his eight man crew building a subgrade near Deep Harbor, Hattie purchased a few sturdy dishes and a new oil cloth for her dining room table and started in business. When the mystic combinations which cause the heavens to open up and furnish copious rains to the earth below failed, Eli fashioned for himself a stone sled, acquired an old white horse and harness, a couple of empty oil drums and a bucket, and started delivery of lake water to the rain barrels.

Perhaps it was by chance that these entries into the uncertainty of untried business endeavor happened in the same year. To complicate the progress and profit of their enterprises, it was the first year of the war. With food rationing and the scarcity of steel drums taxing their ingenuity to the utmost, Hattie and Eli encountered all of the frustrating complexities attendant upon the supply and demand equations of their ventures. Contractors came and went, and in between there were periods of depressing recession. Then too came weeks of abundant rain when the stone sled and the old white horse stood idle in hopeful contemplation of dry spells ahead.

But Hattie and Eli both survived these unpredictable vagaries of service requirements. When it appeared to Hattie that she might as well fold up the table cloth and shelve the surplus dishes, some minor construction project would appear nearby to save the day. When generous rains threatened the well-being of the Wallenon brood and Eli pondered the prudence of seeking employment in the well paying but distant lumber camps, cloudless summer skies or snowless winters would come to the rescue.

By the time that Herr Hitler's ambitious scheme for world domination had shrunk to the perimeter of a beleaguered Berlin and the Asiatic sphere of influence had shrivelled to island hopping, the establishments by now known as Hattie's Boardinghouse and the Deep Harbor Waterworks had become institutions of permanence. The briskness of their service need had shrunk the recessive interruptions to pleasant interludes of rocking chair knitting for Hattie and hunting or fishing for Eli.

Hattie tended her garden and cared for her chickens with the comforting knowledge of money saved by their respective production. The simple fare offered her handful of boarders made up in essential nourishment what it may have lacked in variety or delicacy. No one ever complained about the quality or quantity of the food she supplied. Punctuality was imposed with almost despotic exactitude. Breakfast and supper were served at exactly six. Latecomers were provided for, but they seldom had the temerity to repeat their tardiness. In Hattie's establishment the comforting anticipation of food mingled with an atmosphere of austerity. Her dining room held an oil cloth covered table, eight rickety chairs, and a wood burning black iron stove. The only colors that broke the monotony of drab though neat simplicity were contained in the flower patterned linoleum floor covering and the faded gaiety of figured cotton curtains.

For their meals, the boarders filed into the room in wintry weather and gathered about the heating stove; in summer they sat upon the outer door stoop. No one was so foolhardy as to take his place at the table until the clattering of pots and kettles ceased and Hattie announced, "Alright boys—youse can set."

After a brief period of vigorous attack upon the food at hand, the boarders would file out through the kitchen, picking up their lunch buckets from the work table, and proceed their respective ways. If by chance they chose to linger for a second cup of coffee and to indulge in humorous rail-lery or idle gossip, Hattie would join in with eager readiness and an ability to hold her own; or with good humored ad-monition leaving, however, no doubt of the purport, she would end the session abruptly by saying, "Youse guys gotta get the hell out of here. I got work to do."

Hattie's boarders were a heterogeneous crowd. She fa-vored neither the elite nor the plebeian, the qualification for board being merely the possession of a gainful pursuit in-suring an ability to pay. No special concessions were ever made to the gastronomical preferences or the dietary needs of any boarders. They drank coffee regardless of their de-sire or need for tea, and they ate fried potatoes, ulcers and other digestive disturbances notwithstanding.

Because of the bankrupting influence of a Deep Har-bor Saturday night, board was payable on the line on noon of that day. Inability for the moment to produce the cash was accepted with gracious appreciation of the inevitability of such situations, and did not at all affect the quality or quantity of continued boarding service. Chronic default, however, was met by effective methods entirely original with Hattie Payner.

Eli lived up admirably to the obligation of the public service he sought to render. His was a familiar figure, plod-ding stolidly beside the old white horse dragging a rickety stone sled with several barrels of lake water clinging mirac-ulously to it and sloshing perilously as the primitive vehicle slid over the uneven ground. Laboriously he would transfer the water from his barrels to those of his customers and wait hopefully for his money. Often as not, no change was avail-able, or the customer was not at home, or there was an ar-gument as to the quantity or quality of his deliveries. All this he accepted with understanding resignation as being unavoidable unpleasantries attendant on the prosecution of a business involving public service.

The source of his supply was a shallow, stony beach at the foot of the angling roadway leading from Hugo's to the water front. Eli would prod the old nag to enter the shallow water to a depth affording easy bailing from the lake into the barrels by means of a battered metal bucket. He apparently designed all motions to be as effortless as possible. In winter he had to cut holes in the ice, but they had an irritating tendency to freeze solid overnight.

The barrels were always level full when Eli headed townward from the beach, but the customers got what remained in them when they arrived at their destination. This "loss in transit" was the predominant issue of the daily arguments, but Eli clung tenaciously to his contention that his price was based on full barrels at the water front with the loss in transit being unavoidable shrinkage and properly the expense of the public he served. However sound the economics of this viewpoint, he made it stick; that is, with one exception—his arch enemy, Hattie Payner.

Hattie was not only his best customer, but her boardinghouse was along the path from the water front to the village. There existed between the two a state of inexplicable hostility, punctuated at rare intervals by an equally unaccountable armistice, but flaring more often in profane and vehement imprecation. The latter was particularly amusing to the neighbors and was often stimulated by deliberate indulgence in gossip linking the belligerents. Quite likely both Eli and Hattie derived some measure of enjoyment from this hostility, for both engaged in a very nearly equal amount of aggression.

When it appeared that an uneasy peace prevailed for the moment, Hattie was most certain to find fault with the water delivery. On the other hand, if Eli found the monotony of his daily trudging past the boardinghouse door unrelieved by at least some altercation and name calling, he would craftily fabricate some particularly salacious gossip involving Hattie. Its dispatch to the enemy camp was no problem, since the villagers gloried in scandal and babbling, particularly when it promised to provoke new and entertaining skirmishes. Eli always came out second best.

.   .   .

It was early in the spring. The ferocity of March winds and sleet and snow lingered toward a late departure and the ice covering the water front remained unbroken. Big Island loomed across the strait through a wretched, misty film, while underfoot the melting snow and watery ice imperiled the winter weary villagers.

Rumors of some vast project nearby persisted in the bar rooms and the homes. It would employ a hundred men, some said, and there was great speculation. Women whose husbands had gone *below* to avail themselves of war time wages, found new hope in their possible return to seek employment near homes and families. Hugo, Philo, and Jacques contemplated the probability of greatly increased beer sales and pondered the need for improved bar room furnishings and renovation. Hattie's fortunes were at low ebb, as there had been no construction activities to supply her with boarders in the winter's intense cold and spring's tardy arrival. Eli's fortunes had likewise suffered a prolonged recession brought on by the generous snows of the long, bleak, and often bitter months. All of Deep Harbor was patiently awaiting the end of the uneasy misery and intensified isolation of drifted highways, infrequent mail and supply deliveries, and depressing inactivity. Any rumors of hopeful beneficence to the village were, like the first warm southerly winds or the crashing breakup of the heavy island ice bridge, a stimulant to renewed self respect and ambition.

On the day that the first ore freighters, their new paint glistening on their sleek hulls and smokestacks, crept carefully through the breaking ice fields to begin again a season of picturesque and adventurous commerce, a quiet, unobtrusive man paused briefly at Hugo's to inquire about the possibilities of boarding facilities and rooms in the village. The occupants of drinking booths and hangers-on at the bar strained their ears and maneuvered into better listening positions, while others stared through murky windows to note the baggage and the foreign license on the mud caked, bespattered, and panting vehicle that had brought him. Eli, who during his long and enforced idleness had become quite a card playing, beer guzzling fixture at Hugo's, sensed the import of the occasion and, slipping quietly out the back door, he hastened toward Hattie's boardinghouse.

There existed for the moment one of those rare truces between these two natural antagonists, brought about, no doubt, by mutual commiseration over the long lean months just past. Sitting in Hattie's kitchen behind the wood burning range, Eli expanded proudly and authoritatively upon the portentous news and developments which the stranger's advent signified, while Hattie prepared coffee and piled doughnuts for his ready acceptance. Into her eager ears he poured descriptions of the stranger, his vehicle, and the amount of baggage he carried, and with brazen duplicity repeated how he had hastened to direct the man to her boardinghouse and had emphatically recommended the character of her service and the quality of her food.

While the driving April rain rattled the windows and

drummed violently on the low kitchen roof, they basked contentedly in an atmosphere of chummy comradeship and meditation. They confided in each other their cherished ambitions and desires, the realization of which now appeared within delightful and comfortable nearness. While Hattie thought of a new Easter outfit, Eli boasted of his many capabilities which would doubtlessly obtain for him an important position in this new project, and how he could then escape the drudgery and monotony of water deliveries; in fact, in this new found prosperity he might even be able to afford a housekeeper to care for his obstreperous youngsters.

Elsewhere in the village the news spread like the protest of a disturbed and indignant polecat, accompanied by outrageous overstatement and ridiculous imaginary details. The single iron wire connecting the lonely village to the distant switchboard at Channel City worked overtime as wives frantically placed calls for their laboring spouses in the faraway manufacturing centers. The sole topic of conversation in the bar rooms was the probability of employment opportunities, and every male who had ever wielded a hammer became at once a self styled craftsman, or possessed other talents of importance likely to be greatly in demand. Housewives speculated upon the rent they should receive for rooms and set up rate scales at ridiculously inflated prices. The local preachers viewed the stringency of their budgets in the light of greater Sunday collections, while the local merchant leafed hopefully through unpaid and long overdue grocery bills.

Whatever the expectations of the townsfolk, they were not disappointed when it came. The beer halls flourished, and the debauchery of primitive isolation assumed the most uninhibited proportions. Spontaneous street brawls originating in local antipathies gained frequency and ferocity as the influx of strangers swelled the beer guzzling crowds in the bar rooms. Internecine quarrels of craftsmen and local laborers came as construction progressed. The village selectmen viewed the situation with undisturbed detachment, while the State constabulary wearied of the repeated calls for its assistance. The meaning of the development provoked no thoughts of the probable permanent effects upon a hitherto jobless, decadent community. Everyone had jingling money in his pocket, and the horizon of thought reached not at all to benefits accruing for the future.

Eli purchased a saw, square, hammer, and nail apron, together with a union card, and as an accepted journeyman found full employment and consequent opulence. He acquired a housekeeper and continued as a sideline the water service to which the villagers had become accustomed. The six motherless urchins apparently thrived in an undisciplined atmosphere of rowdiness and mischief undeterred by the acquisition of household supervision. Eli's days were spent at work on the construction project, while in the early evening hours he delivered water. This service was no longer performed in a spirit of humility, his easy circumstances having prompted an arrogant independence. Any complaint of service, quality, or quantity was settled promptly by complete suspension of deliveries. That is, with the exception of Hattie.

What measure of prosperity the construction of the new mine brought to Deep Harbor accrued also to Hattie's boardinghouse. Without increasing her original facilities for eight, she now served in shifts. As construction progress changed the character of skills required, so also was the character of her boarders changed. First came the site preparation crews, followed in remarkably rapid succession by the carpenters, plumbers, electricians, steel workers, and millwrights. Each new group provided a delightful opportunity for Hattie to tell and retell with minute detail the story of her childhood, her marriage, the circumstances of her widowhood, and the shortcomings of her fellow townsfolk. She gloried in scandal and gossip, and with elaborate imagination she expanded knowingly upon the intimate history and ancestry of her neighbors, not excepting Eli Wallenon and his six depredating youngsters.

Her comparative prosperity obliterated all of Hattie's former condescension and there was added to the simple austerity of her establishment a subtle arrogance. It was as if she were aware of the indispensability of her services in the construction drama for which Deep Harbor at the moment was the stage.

.   .   .

This is not a narrative of the industrialization of a northwoods village, nor a revelation of a backward community shocked from apathetic insensibility to reality into a drama it could neither become responsive to nor understand. Construction projects, like dramas, end, but with a slow, unspectacular, and hesitant cessation, not with the crashing applause of a last curtain. When the last construction equipment left the site of its recent Herculean activity near Deep Harbor, the village remained as before, a collection of ungainly houses huddled along an unpaved thoroughfare, graced by its three motley beer halls, its dejection and soullessness alleviated only by the spiritual courage of its two churches.

.   .   .

The completed mine and its processing plant dipped into the local labor supply with cautious selectivity. Unlike the construction activity that had preceded it, it was not wedded to nor identified with Deep Harbor. The village was but an accident of proximity. Employment started slowly. The war being over, it recruited its labor force unhurriedly from the returning servicemen, the bush, and the surrounding lumber camps. It screened the local self styled artisans with care and exactitude and with disconcerting deliberation. Its labor importations were few, and in consequence Hattie's once flourishing establishment shrank to a handful of unattached itinerants. Eli, in spite of the acquired tools of his asserted calling, flunked the skillful inquisition of the employment manager and in consequence, became completely dependent upon his water delivery service for sorely needed income. The natural transition of Deep Harbor to normalcy revived its traditional antipathies, not the least of these being the entertaining hostility between Hattie Payner and Eli Wallenon.

The "boys," as Hattie called her six steady boarders, had finished their evening meal and were sitting on the front door stoop awaiting the arrival of the daily mail bus. As men are wont to do, they were digging up stories and anecdotes of ancient vintage dressed up in modern verbiage which in no wise added to their acceptance in a more decorous group. They all commenced with the usual "Did you hear the one about . . ." Hattie, who enjoyed this sort of thing with relish and who knew a few stories herself, sat just out of sight within the doorway in her favorite rocker, straining her ears so that no choice bit might escape her. She was not entirely successful in suppressing her mirth, however, and the "boys" were fully aware of her eavesdropping. But they had been in Deep Harbor long enough to understand its worldliness and sophistication and were therefore undeterred by any propriety or chivalrous delicacy.

On this particular evening, abetted by the tardiness of

the mail truck, the stories were numerous and reached new heights of spice and ribaldry. Bud Taylor, in more serious moments a rather efficient welder, was relating one, the context of which was not only long but also provocative of the most salacious anticipation. In the midst of his discourse, while Hattie leaned forward to catch its startling disclosure, a loud and insistent banging on the back door commanded her immediate attention.

Irritated by this untimely interruption of an especially promising story, whose valuable addition to her well stocked repertoire of similar tales she was already envisioning, Hattie flung open the door to confront none other than the grinning countenance of Eli Wallenon, who had chosen this unpropitious moment to refill her rain barrels.

It may have been the wrath in Hattie's eyes that provoked the mockery in Eli's grin or it may have been the mockery in Eli's grin that provoked the wrath in Hattie's eyes, but it was Eli who supplied the spark that set off this explosive combination. With brazen indifference to the probable consequence, he blandly asked, "Whatsamatter, Hattie, burn the gravy again?"

Then, noting with satisfaction that for once in a lifetime of feuding he had rendered his opponent wordless, Eli turned his back and with impudent nonchalance commenced transferring the water. Delayed action, however, only served to increase the explosive force when it came. Eli was entirely unprepared for the unmerciful barrage of invective that engulfed him, nor had he ever before experienced it so scathingly profane and fluent. Nor could he get a word in to recapture the offensive. Often before he had heard his ancestry described in barnyard vernacular, and himself pilloried as a "wife killing widow cheating flea bitten swamp hog." But when Hattie, fairly trembling with the pressure of her rage, as a parting blast referred to his offspring as "swill guzzling bastards of a square headed Swede," it was too much for his Finnish temperament. With an angry grunt Eli flung the bucket at Hattie's feet, picked up the reins, clucked to his sleepy steed, and started off.

But Hattie was not finished yet. She seized the bucket and with power and accuracy greatly to her credit, flung it at Eli's defenseless head. Eli ducked, but he might better have taken it. With a resounding smack it bounced off the rump of the unsuspecting steed who, despite the inertia of his great age, leaped frightened into his frail worn harness, scattering stone sled, barrels, water, and Eli all over Hattie's weedgrown and littered backyard.

Eli got up slowly and soberly. Hattie, shocked into complete immobility by the disastrous consequences, or perhaps by the apparent completeness, of her victory, failed to recognize the menace in her approaching victim. She had barely time enough for a profane shriek before Eli seized her about the waist, folded her like a jackknife, and plunged her stern first into her own water barrel. And from this ignominious predicament she was rescued a few moments later by her six grinning boarders.

.   .   .

The next morning breakfast was, as always, at six. The customary "Youse guys can set," however, lacked its usual authoritative diction. The six boarders filed in quietly and took their accustomed places. As it was every day, the glass of canned fruit juice stood ready, next to a plate containing two slices of toast and a cube of margarine. And before each man was a platter from which two eggs stared upward exactly as they had done yesterday, last week, and last month.

There was the usual can of condensed milk for coffee, and the salt and pepper placed conveniently within reach. There was the same silence as the "boys" gulped down the food at hand. As always before, Hattie poured the second cup of coffee for each, but with averted eyes and without the customary wisecracking prattle. Always before, when plates were pushed back and a cigarette accompanied the second cup of coffee, lively banter would spring unbidden to enliven the few moments remaining before departure to the daily labors. Not so this morning after a fateful night before.

Bud Taylor sought to break the oppressive silence by some pointless remark, but it served only to intensify the consciousness of an embarrassed tension. Bert Swensen, a husky laborer with a bald head, sat across from Taylor. Always before he had been fair game for good natured ridicule pertaining principally to his shiny pate, to which he usually responded in heavy Scandinavian accent and surprisingly adaptive repartee. But on this morning no barbs of derision came his way and he ate in unmolested silence.

John Purdy and Tom Kelly kept their eyes on their plates or watched the smoke curl lazily from their cigarettes and said nothing. John's recent sojourn in a state prison for a crime offensive even to the frail moral senses of the others had been ferretted out by Hattie to the end that he shunned any words or deeds that might direct attention to himself. Tom, on the other hand, was when sober a past master at buffoonery. But his propensity to arrive for Saturday and Sunday supper in an extreme state of befuddlement had culminated in an infraction that even the most liberal of house manners could hardly forgive. He was permitted to continue as a guest only on the express promise never again to appear at the table in such a condition that he mistake the gravy bowl for a pillow. Far be it from Tom

Kelly to risk even the most inoffensive pun in the straitened atmosphere of this particular breakfast after a hard won and rather precarious probation.

At the far end of the table, apart from the rest, sat Licky Wallace. His aloneness stemmed from his extremely slovenly table manners, his aversion to soap and water, and his stunted mental state. His presence as a guest was one of those inexplicable quirks of Hattie's mental makeup. His name was prompted by his habit of lapsing into an absent minded trance, in which condition he wolfed his food, clutching the meat in his soiled fingers, the while scooping up his potatoes in the palm of his grimy hand. After completing his meal he carefully licked each finger, unmindful of the often cruel jibes of his fellow boarders. Hattie supplied Licky with plates, cups, and utensils solely for his own use, set on a newspaper placed over the precious oil cloth to protect it from the filth and grime of his never laundered clothing. Because of his habit of licking the top of the catsup bottle and scooping the sugar from the bowl with his fingers, she guarded against the justifiable objections of the other boarders by a catsup bottle, sugar bowl, and other condiments carefully identified as being for Licky's use alone. The rest of the boarders, unable to understand Hattie's tolerance, ribbed her good humoredly about her probable kinship to the witless fool or of having matrimonial designs. This day, however, no torment was directed to Licky's end of the table, nor were any witticisms about kinship or marriage possibilities mentioned for Hattie's benefit.

Eric Dalton was the youngest boarder. He worked in a labor-clerical capacity that no doubt contributed to his unbounded conceit and self esteem. Mostly ignored by his fellow boarders, he nevertheless projected himself into any table conversation, whether it was serious, humorous, or just gossip. He was referred to variously as a smart aleck, a wise-cracking fool, or just plain pest. Such allusions to his personal qualities deterred him not at all. The atmosphere of this unusual breakfast was one of guilt and soul searching, forbidding even the thought of flippancy. But fools will leap where angels fear to tread, and Eric was no angel. Pouring himself some water, he lifted the glass, squinted at it speculatively, and with foolhardy audacity blurted, "I suppose this is some of the water Hattie took her bath in last night."

The atmosphere up to now had an uncomfortable tenseness about it, but the stunned, chilly silence that followed this artless remark was beyond endurance. If Hattie had only delivered a barrage of crockery or kitchenware, or exploded with characteristic profanity and fluent imprecations, all six of the boarders would have welcomed the happy return to boardinghouse normalcy. Instead, however, Hattie stood staring in icy silence, arms akimbo, the rage in her eyes penetrating the souls of the six defenseless and very frightened men. In silence they slinked by her, picked up their lunch buckets, and hurried to their work.

When evening came, the "boys" gathered as usual on Hattie's front door stoop. Conversation lagged, perhaps by reason of the apprehension that permeated their thought. Six o'clock came, but not so the usual punctual call to "set." The minutes passed all too quickly, to confirm misgivings that had dogged their thinking through the day. The mail truck clattered to a stop at the post office. Bud Taylor took the initiative by rising, and with brave resolve rapped loudly on the door. There was no response. Nor was there to be the next day or the days that followed.

.   .   .

On an evening a week later, Bud Taylor, Tom Kelly, and Bert Swensen, all who remained of the original six, sat dejectedly on the post office steps munching store cookies and chocolate bars. Their stomachs had long since revolted against sardines, canned soups, and the other scanty fare that was available on the sparse shelves of the local general store. Tom was buried deep in thought, a reverie which no doubt related to meat, potatoes, and gravy. Bud was rolling a cigarette with absent minded deliberation, thinking perhaps of its delectable association with a cup of steaming hot coffee. Across the broad strait the smoke curled lazily from the tall stack of the power plant that served the huge new mine on Big Island. The cool evening breeze carried across the water the faint roar of mine machinery. A giant ore carrier, its white foredeck and long black hull reflecting the brilliance of the setting sun, blew a deep, hoarse whistle blast to signal its course to a steamer approaching it from the blueness of the great lake *below*. All was framed in the deep green softness of the dense forests and the dark blue island headlands.

Under other circumstances, the scene would have delighted the latent artistry of the simplest of souls. Not so, however, for the hungry and despairing three.

Tom Kelly broke the silence with an excited cry. "Cripes almighty, jeez, what the hell you know about this!"

Then he read from the weekly Deep Harbor column:

Hattie Payner and Eli Wallenon, both of Deep Harbor, were united in marriage today in the chambers of the County Circuit Court. The happy couple expect to make their home in Deep Harbor at the bride's house in which she formerly operated a boarding service. Mr. Wallenon has a fine position in the cedar post cutting business. The marriage is a culmination of many years of pleasant neighborly association and friendship. They will be at home to their many friends after a brief honeymoon in Channel City.

Tom continued reading:

Robert Spengleman of Conners Corners has taken a contract to drill several wells for residents of Deep Harbor.

and

Allen Carson, recently discharged from the army where he has seen long and severe service, is opening a restaurant in Deep Harbor. He expects to specialize in steaks and chops, catering also to special parties and family dinners.

Tom tossed the paper high in the air and let forth a piercing, joyous whoop. Bud jumped to his feet and danced a fancy jig, ending with an awkward pirouette. Bert Swensen ended his reverie with a broad, anticipatory smile and with ecstasy unconcealed by his weighty accent said, "Smörgåsbord too, maybe?"

THE KETTLE ISLAND AFFAIR

PHIL SPERRY wasn't exactly an angel; on the other hand, he wasn't too bad when compared with the thieving, racketeering underworld of Motor City. At middle age he had at least a few accomplishments with which to be satisfied. He had married at an early age and had raised a son to maturity despite marital strife, some infidelity, and considerable heavy drinking. He had become quite skillful and self-sustaining as a blacksmith. True, he had seen frequent periods of unemployment due to the occasional economic setbacks that plague heavy industrial centralization such as that of Motor City. However, these lean periods often as not were the results of domestic difficulties abetted by protracted bouts and strong drink and loose women.

When the war came, Phil's craft was much in demand and his employment was full and profitable. His wife obtained work as a riveter in an aircraft plant and his son departed for the service. The family unit, never too stable under the best of circumstances, improved not at all under the impetus of dual income and decreasing domestic complexities occasioned by the departure of the only child.

As the war neared its end, the family unit disintegrated entirely, and probably to the satisfaction of both parties. This must also have been the case with the third party, since upon his discharge from the service he did not even bother to come home.

On a mid-May morning in a postwar year, Phil, unemployed at the moment, sober for a change, and broke, contemplated his future and took stock of himself. He was not exactly married, but yet he was not quite single, having had some sort of a paper served on him indicating that divorce proceedings had been undertaken by his wife. That did not worry him.

His sole possessions consisted of a battered old car and an equally battered house trailer. The latter was his present residence. This he shared on occasion, with brazen disregard for the entangling complexities that might be involved, with whatever homeless female he might meet in the various bar rooms. He never bothered to determine their marital status and, for that matter, neither did his various cohabitants inquire into his. The only qualifications seemed to be mutual loneliness, mutual convenience, and momentary unattachment.

Being a smart man, Phil also gave regard to these spurious connubial arrangements from the standpoint of social security and unemployment compensation. The extreme mobility of his domicile arrangements served a good purpose in that he could escape residential identification by the simple expedient of moving to another trailer parking lot. This ingenious device also took care of momentary difficulties arising from some irate but legal husband discovering the unfaithfulness of his erring spouse.

On this particular mid-May morning, Phil had need to study his personal situation in the light of some extremely pressing entanglements. For one thing, his most recently acquired consort while eminently satisfactory had, after a few weeks, brought into his rather crowded living quarters three illegitimate children, aged two, nine, and sixteen. For the moment this had its financial advantages in that the state, with misplaced liberality though probably humanitarian intent, placed a premium on illegitimacy by providing generously for the support of the unfortunate youngsters. Furthermore, it placed the management of the funds in the hands of the poor "wronged" mother under, of course, the watchful eye of an over-worked and under-manned welfare department.

Phil, pressing as always for financial advantages, cunningly included this family in his dependency statement. This added eight dollars weekly to his basic unemployment benefits. All of this added up to capitalistic achievement but—it also added up to trouble. If the inquiries recently made about him at the trailer camp indicated anything at all, that trouble was near at hand.

And so Phil, on this pleasant morning, came to some sound conclusions, not the least of which was the need for terminating his present connubial as well as family relationship and getting himself and his mobile possessions as far away from Motor City as space and time would allow.

Sundown found him already far away from the smoke and grime, the noise and litter, and his vexatious personal problems.

.   .   .

Over on Big Island, the new mine had commenced operation. Plagued by the postwar shortage of materials, its first month of single shift operation was far from spectacular. Man power and more man power was needed as the mine limped haltingly into its second month of production.

God had blessed this magnificent country with an abundance of space and beauty. But mines are not run by islands, rivulets, azure skies, or by lakes and bays and pretty forests. Mines are run by men trained to press the buttons and pull the levers of mechanical monsters, exacting from them instant obedience to perform Herculean tasks. They are run by men skilled in administering to the ills and foibles of intricate machinery of iron, of pulsing arteries of copper, lead, and steel, of cavernous stomachs of hissing, boiling mass digestion, of lungs that inhale with the roar of tempests and expel with the biting rasp of machine guns. Men such as these are not found running foot-loose and unattached in a country of the bush and forest.

In a frantic effort to get production on a three shift operation as quickly as possible, the mine management had combed the sparse and widely scattered population to employ the best of the talent and skill available.

From a tiny sheet iron office located temporarily on the mainland directly across the strait from the huge mine site, the mine manager looked out upon the dazzling waters to the distant headlands beyond Island Bay. It was a lovely June morning. The fresh greenness of the newly unfolded hardwood leaves blended in pleasing contrast with the deeper shade of the spruce and balsam and the clean whiteness of the birches. Not far away, a pair of loons floated majestically on the placid surface, now and then diving in their characteristically deliberate manner. Here and there on the smooth surface could be seen and heard the brief flash and splash of huge game fish, leaving evidence of their playfulness in the rhythmic ringlets that broke the mirrored surface. A few hundred yards offshore on tiny Kettle Island were a dozen odd urchins who had risked the penalties of truancy rather than to miss the delights of the perch run that this beautiful morning offered. It was a perfect day—for fishing.

To the mine manager it was like any other day—a day of problems. There were problems of transportation of much needed supplies and repair parts from the far distant railhead. There were problems of communication across the lovely strait to the vital island plant, for which submarine equipment long overdue was needed. There were problems of man power, of supervisory personnel, of mine safety, and of housing.

He glanced idly at the reports of the preceding day. They spoke of breakdowns, of production interruptions, of maintenance failures, of absenteeism, of carelessness, and of human indolence. On the bottom of one report was a notation explaining the steadily declining supply of blasted ore. That same notation had appeared yesterday, the day before, and for a week before that. It stated, in a most understandable way,

Them guys in the shop aint gittin them bits sharpened and tempered so to stand up on hard ground drillin. The pit will be outta blasted ore by next sattiday.

Yes, the pits would be out of ore by the weekend and then the plant would have to curtail even its present single shift, all for want of a blacksmith skilled in tempering steel —a sorry picture to contemplate on a good fishing day.

The manager reached for the telephone. The dull absence of a reassuring hum told him that, as often before, the single iron wire connecting Deep Harbor with the Channel City switchboard was dead. He flung the receiver violently into its cradle and savagely tore open a package of cigarettes. Lighting one, he strode to the window giving view to the mine across the strait and growled aloud, "Anyone that's blasted fool enough to open a mine on a lousy island way up in a god forsaken wilderness like this shouldn't be running loose."

Turning to the opposite window that overlooked the shabby village, he continued, "And they blew up a pretty South Pacific atoll and a couple hundred goats and pigs just to try out the atom bomb when they could have saved themselves and me too a lot of trouble if they'd just've blown this god awful cesspool clean out of the United States."

Feeling better, the mine manager strode back to his desk, tossed his papers into a brief case, and walked out to the launch to go across to the mine.

As he was boarding the boat, a voice hailed him. He turned to see a stocky middle aged man, carrying a fishing pole, walking toward him. "Mister, what's that big works over on the island? Some sort of a mine?"

Being assured that it was, the man continued, "Who you gotta see bout a job over there?"

The mine manager paused a moment, then turned back to the office and beckoned the man to follow him. Seated at his desk with the man sitting across from him, the manager contemplated his newest prospect. "Where you from?" he asked.

"Down *below*."

"What are you doing up in this country?"

"Oh, I been workin' down *below* a long time. Lost my wife now, and kinda thought I'd take some time off an' get me some fishin'. Noticed that place over there and bein' tired of fishin' and loafin' and kinda likin' the country up here, thought mebbe I might get me a job and stay here."

"Where are you staying?"

"Got me a trailer set up about a mile south a' here," the man replied.

The manager contemplated this for a moment. Such cases were rare. Here was a man looking for a job and there was no housing or boarding problem involved. He asked, "What kind of work you been doing?"

"Oh, a little bit of everything. Been operatin' cranes, runnin' tractors, but mostly I been blacksmithin'."

"Blacksmithing? What kind of blacksmithing?"

"Oh, all kinds. Mostly sharpenin' drill bits, temperin' steel, and such like," was the reply.

The manager had to reach for a cigarette and it was a real effort for him to maintain his composure. "What's your name?" he asked.

"Phil Sperry."

The manager fumbled with a card, made a few entries, and said, "Okay, Phil, you report on the seven o'clock boat in the morning to my office on the mine site."

Phil looked at him with genuine gratitude in his tanned face. "Well mister, I sure want to thank you," he said and he went out.

The manager looked down at his desk and then at the receding figure of Phil Sperry. "He thanks me and I should

kiss him," he said, "gosh almighty, one more deal like this
and dammed if I won't join a church."

.   .   .

June passed and the mine did not shut down for want
of tempered steel. From the pits came an ever swelling avalanche of blasted ore. A second shift and then a third was
needed to quicken the mills that ground and graded and
stored the ore. Phil Sperry's expertly tempered bits rang
true and sound and the silence of Big Island was shattered
by the detonations of high explosives, the snorting grunts of
power shovels, and the hum and roar of cars and locomotives.

Giant freighters, their bows held proud and high,
swung into position to load the oar, and left a few hours
hence, their long sleek sides deep in the water, their haugh-
tiness bowed in submission to the burden they carried.

One morning the mine manager was studying the production reports, noting with increasing satisfaction and
pride the progress being made. A light step at the door and
a hesitant knock drew his attention. It was Phil Sperry. A
stray lock of hair hung down on his perspiring forehead and
across his face was a black smudge attesting to his calling.

"Mister," he began, "could I get my withholdin' papers changed?"

"Sure thing," replied the manager as he rummaged in
his desk for the necessary forms. "What happened, did you
get yourself a wife?"

"Yep," Phil beamed, relieved by the apparent simplicity of the fiscal arrangements which an increase or decrease
of dependents seemed to imply. Then, while he scrawled
his signature on the papers, he continued, "Yep, it's a
woman I knowed down *below*. She's comin' tonight and

we spect to get married at Channel City tomorrer, if you can let me get off work a half day."

"That's okay by me, Phil. Hope you'll both be happy. And by the way, where are you going to live?"

Phil beamed again. "In my trailer. It's big enough for two. Besides, I got me a tarp so's to have a kind of porch to do the cookin' in."

"I see. Will your wife like living in a trailer?"

"Oh sure, she lived in it with me before down *below*." Then he quickly added, "We allus figured on bein' married some time soon as I had me a good job." Pausing as if he had neglected something important, Phil added, "I like my job, mister, and I like workin' for this outfit, and I hope I kin allus keep workin' here."

To this the mine manager replied, his voice concealing the sincerity of his words, "We like having you working for us too, Phil, and good luck to you."

As the bulky figure of Phil Sperry disappeared around the office building, the manager whistled a soft tune suspiciously like "Will you love me in September as you did in May," and then said to himself, "One half the world don't know how the other half lives, nor cares." With that he settled down to the day's problems.

Bolts, nuts, boiler compound, dynamite, lumber, oil, grease—the list seemed endless, and the mine's capacity for consuming these many items seemed insatiable. A labor dispute, boat schedules, insurance renewals, government reports, contracts, safety surveys, bureaucratic hearings, injury reports, and when at last the bottom of the pile was reached there stared him in the face the Kettle Island matter. The mine manager propped his feet on the desk and pondered.

Kettle Island was owned by the mine company. A

scrawny acre of rocky land, sparsely covered with scraggly trees, it lay a few hundred yards off the mainland shore. On it was a dilapidated house, its windows and doors long since the victims of local acquisitiveness.

Close to the navigating channels of the strait, the island was a menace. It served no useful purpose—that is, from the standpoint of the mine. To the tax powers of the local assessor it appeared to have a fabulous relationship to the otherwise useless, barren, valueless land areas.

When all other problems for the day seemed satisfactorily disposed of, the question of what to do with this white elephant defeated any thought of relaxation and peace of mind. Here it was again, a tantalizing problem that defied solution. With irritating regularity came the letters from the mine owners.

> We hope that you will soon give us your recommendations as to the satisfactory disposal of Kettle Island. We cannot urge too strongly the necessity for putting this property to some useful purpose or of disposing of it in some manner that will relieve us of the taxes.

"And they bombed beautiful Bikini!" the mine manager snorted.

A week after the nuptials, legal or assumed, of Phil Sperry, there came again a hesitant knock on the door of the office. It was Phil. His face bore none of the beatific happiness of a bridegroom nor the confident air of a satisfied and satisfactory workman. "Mister," he began, betraying troubled thoughts and pressing problems, "I gotta get me a place to live."

The manager turned this information over in his mind and said, "What's the matter? Trailer not big enough since you got married?"

"No, mister, it ain't just that. But you see the woman I married has got three kids, and they spect to be here on the mail bus tonight and I gotta get me a house or barn or sumthin' for the trailer don't sleep only two."

Sparring for time and thinking in terms of tempered bits and full production, the manager asked, "Three kids, eh? How old?"

Phil had to think for a moment. Then he replied, "The youngest is a girl two, the next is a boy nine, and the oldest is a girl sixteen."

The manager whistled. "Man, you sure accumulated a family in a hurry. Been looking around any to see if you could find a shack?"

"No," replied Phil. Then, his face brightening as if a ray of hope had for the moment penetrated the deep gloom of his predicament, he added, "Ain't no place to be got as far as I kin see. Been wondrin' bout mebbe I could rent that house on that island they call Kettle or sumthin'."

It was the manager's turn to brighten. "But Phil, that place has no windows or doors. How in hell are you going to keep a wife and three kids on there? And if you could, what are you going to do, swim to work every morning and back every night?"

Phil had a ready answer. "Oh, that's alright, mister. I been over and looked at it and for bout thirty dollars I guiss I kin fix it up good nuff to live in. And I know where I kin buy me a boat for ten dollars."

The manager mulled this over in his mind. "Okay, Phil, I'll tell you what I'll do. You fix it up so it satisfies you and I'll let you live rent free. I'll pay for window glass and a couple of doors. You put them in." He paused and then added, "With that family increase maybe you better make out another withholding form."

Reaching for the form, the manager said, "Let's see—there is you, your wife, and three children, making five exemptions all told, right?"

Phil beamed. "Well, mister, there's really six. My wife's oldest daughter has got herself a six month old baby. Don't you rightly think I should get credit for that exemption too?"

"Okay, Phil, it's six. And good luck to you."

After Phil left, the manager took a quick check of the remaining correspondence. He glanced at the latest Kettle Island letter from the mine owners. "We cannot urge too strongly the necessity of putting this property to some useful purpose," and so forth. He tossed the letter into the file basket muttering, "Useful purpose, hell. I'm sharpening bits with the damn thing right now, but I'm wondering if there isn't such a thing as jumping from the Kettle into the fire or something."

.   .   .

It was early August and a delightfully cool late afternoon. The mine manager sat on the post office steps among the crowds awaiting the evening mail. The sun was still above the tree line and its slanting rays reflected a rainbow hue on the islands low on the eastern horizon. A freighter, its sunlit hull shining in exaggerated contrast to the darkening waters of the strait, was making a long turn to land at the Big Island ore dock. A second freighter was backing astern to clear the mine wharf with its cargo, bound for ports far *below*, while a Coast Guard cutter blew a recognition signal. The vessels answered in turn and when the last echo from the deep resonance of their friendly interchange of salutations died in the vastness of the scenic area, a silence prevailed, unbroken except by the occasional snatches of conversation among the waiting people. The stillness was refreshing and pleasant, with dignity in keeping with the majesty of the view.

As if to profane this scene, a startling crash of a heavy door and raucous laughter punctuated with piercing feminine screams and unabashed merriment drew the attention of the waiting crowd. From Philo's bar room staggered Slim Crawford. On each of his arms was an unkempt woman, followed by two equally inebriated and well known town bums. The staggering quintette picked its way across the dusty roadway, weaving and staggering, voicing lewd invective, and screaming derisively at the waiting crowd. Then it fell in a writhing heap with a shameless exposure of scantily clad feminine limbs and indecent pantomime.

Such scenes were not unusual in Deep Harbor and, in consequence, provoked much laughter rather than a sense of civic shame. The antics of Slim Crawford contributed a frequent measure of amusement, as also did those of his two male companions. However, the two women provoked curiosity and question, being, as it happened, strangers in this August evening's exhibit.

Wagging tongues soon brought forth identification. They were the wife and daughter of a recently hired mine employee who had taken over the Kettle Island house for his residence.

To the mine manager this was startling and disconcerting information. Its impact upon his peace of mind was in no way softened when he remembered that his highly prized blacksmith was at that very moment working on the second shift. Thoughtfully he watched the five participants weaving their way out of sight toward the water front.

Working late that night in his mainland office, the mine manager heard a rhythmic rippling on the water fol-

lowed by a loud splash and an agonized grunt. Seizing a
flashlight, he saw a dark and bobbing figure swimming toward him from the direction of Kettle Island. A moment
later he dragged from the cold water the sodden, half clad
figure of one of his first shift millmen. No words were exchanged. The bedraggled figure slinked away, but not before the manager noted the bruised face and the stark terror
in his eyes. The manager looked at his watch. It was just
past midnight. Phil, he reflected, would have arrived at his
Kettle Island home about half an hour ago.

The next morning the manager found a note pinned
to the office door. It was from the rescued mill hand and
stated briefly and significantly, "I quit. Mail my check to
General Delivery, Motor City." Yes indeed, from the Kettle into the fire.

The manager noted thereafter with growing apprehension the water traffic from the mainland to the island.
Punts, canoes, logs, rafts, and decrepit rowboats conveyed
an ever increasing male clientele. It was by no means a selected clientele, nor did their visits always coincide with
Phil's working shifts. His misgivings were in no wise eased
by the occasional absences of his blacksmith which inquiry
revealed were due to hangovers. The women appeared often in the local bar rooms and frequently enacted ludicrously inebriated scenes of sordid immodesty, much to the
amusement of the male population.

The town, of course, buzzed and the tongues of appre-
hensive wives wagged. Before long no husband was above
suspicion and the petty jealousies of mischief minded busy-
bodies provoked vague rumors which from constant repetition become realities that raised scandal mongering eyebrows to new levels of outraged virtue. Very often such
rumors had bases in fact, and for this more than one erring

husband suffered the humiliation of a wifely beating before an unsympathetic as well as amused populace.

Sermons of the aroused clergymen served only to advertise the bacchanalian orgies and delightful diversions obtainable on the now famed Kettle Island. The crews of vessels docking at the mine to load ore learned of its recreational facilities. Owners of motor driven boats and launches in consequence found a new source of revenue in ferrying shore leave crew members to and from this oasis of uninhibited pleasures.

As usual in crises that commanded the attention of elected city fathers, these selectmen side-stepped their civic responsibility. Kettle Island was not Deep Harbor and in the comforting knowledge of lack of jurisdiction, they continued their apathy, as well as their amusement.

The state constabulary entered the picture but found federal jurisdiction a barrier to concerted exercise of police power, which in turn pleased the county sheriff no end since he had been under pressure for action which he had neither the desire nor the courage to perform. Yes—the Kettle was boiling.

The Sperry women did not conceal their opulence in their enterprise. They bought liquor by the case and clad themselves in frilly silk garments. But frills and silk concealed not at all the filth and stench of unwashed bodies, nor the depravity and dissipation of low moral levels.

If Phil profited at all by the briskness of the Kettle Island activity, it was not evident in his worldly possessions. He drank more frequently, and his drinking bouts became more protracted.

The frequent appearance of battered noses and bruised faces among the villagers and mine workers indicated something more than feminine pugnacity. Frisked pockets and empty wallets after paydays indicated that the Kettle Island enterprise had borrowed some of the technique of the Motor City underworld.

An outraged citizenry lacked only a militant leadership to assert itself in an unrestrained lynching. Perhaps luckily so such leadership was lacking in this backwoods village. Instead they sought a scapegoat and upon the uneasy head of the mine manager they descended in force, blaming this infringement on the frail morality and decency of the village upon the selfish greed of the mine.

And among the loudest and most vehement were Hugo, Jacques, and Philo. Indeed, the lid of the Kettle was about to blow off.

The mine manager pondered the situation, then acted. Tempered steel, drilled, ground, and blasted ore notwithstanding, he fired Phil Sperry. And Phil, the canny refugee from Motor City, quietly disappeared—leaving his family behind him and the problem of Kettle Island still staring the manager squarely in the face.

The manager acted quickly and decisively. A few mornings later, the welfare authorities of the state arrived upon the scene, sized up the situation, and soon departed, taking with them three vermin ridden and filthy youngsters.

Inquiry in legal circles revealed only scant hope for successful eviction proceedings, and then only by means of amazingly intricate and long drawn out processes. There were ever present the aggravating questions of jurisdictional authority and the reluctance of elected peace officers to enter into the moral affairs of a primitive and lawless backwoods community. If through this maze of ponderous though lawful action eventual relief from a sordid affair were at last obtained, the two sirens conducting their island emporium of delight would have meanwhile enjoyed several months of unhindered and profitable respite. "And," added the manager, "by that time God help the morals of Deep Harbor."

Thereupon he drew his portable typewriter toward him. He inserted a sheet of legal foolscap that had the disturbing appearance of the majesty of law even though it lacked any basis of legal power. Laboriously he typed a hodgepodge of legal verbiage beginning with "Know ye by these presents" and ending with "the sovereign state of," and so forth and "the will of the people." He forged a few signatures, dressed up the document with an enchanting blue cover, and smudged it with sealing wax and a few pieces of gold tinsel. A few moments later he stepped into a rowboat and cast off.

As he rowed slowly but with determination toward Kettle Island, the manager could see the doors of village houses open, and feminine occupants shading their eyes to better identify the latest addition to the Kettle Island clientele. On the back porch of the water front boardinghouse he could see Hattie training a pair of field glasses upon him. Under his breath he muttered, "Nuts."

A few minutes later Mrs. Sperry, alias Mrs. White, alias Pearl Brown tore his carefully prepared legal summons into shreds and threw them into his face with a shrill voiced reference to the indiscretion of his ancestry.

·   ·   ·

The next morning breakfast was as usual at Hattie's boardinghouse. His fellow boarders cast sidelong grimaces at the manager, and Hattie flopped a pair of eggs sunny side up on his plate. With a sly smirk on her face and for the benefit of all present, she whispered, "I see youse got some new lady friends."

"Nuts," grunted the mine manager.

As he walked down to his water front office that morning the mail bus was just departing. Feminine voices hailed him. Leaning from the open window of the outward bound bus, Mrs. Sperry alias White alias Brown and her slattern daughter, in all of their accumulated and gaudy finery, blew him an affectionate kiss punctuated by indescribably obscene gestures. He watched the bus climb the winding road and disappear in a cloud of dust, then continued wearily to his office.

On his desk was the morning mail. An inter-office letterhead was at the top of the heap. The manager picked it up and read it. The last paragraph read, "We are still awaiting your recommendations for some disposition of the Kettle Island property," and so forth. Viciously he tossed the paper into the file basket, took a deep breath, and, as if to relieve the pressure of profound and weary exasperation, exploded, "NUTS!"

NEITHER SLEET NOR STORM
NOR DARK OF NIGHT . . .

SAM PARIS, operator of the Deep Harbor supply truck and carrier of the single mail sack that departed each morning at eight for distant Channel City, parked his battered vehicle in front of the general store and post office to take last minute orders from a handful of housewives. Hattie, clad in early morning attire with a man's overcoat thrown over her, wanted a couple of spools of thread. Jack Baker's wife, expecting as usual, wanted him to pick up a bolt of muslin. "Don't forgit it, cuz this kid is due any time and I ain't got no diapers fixed for it," the disheveled woman admonished him. Percy Forrest wanted a bottle of liniment, and with painful grimaces he impressed Sam with his dire need for it.

The local postmaster, Tom Sanderson, didn't have the mail sack completed yet, so Sam leaned against the fender and looked out across the frozen strait for some hints as to weather possibilities. One did that up here in the Northland where winters gloried in surprises that frequently wrought serious consequences for those who needed to travel the seventy bleak miles to Channel City each day.

It had been a fairly mild winter with frequent thaws. In consequence, snow cover, except in the woods, was scant and the gravel highway was in good condition. For many years Sam had pushed the supply truck through these dreary miles, often under conditions that would frighten the best of drivers. Ground hog day was now close at hand and the month of March, after a mild January and February, could drive the most intrepid into shelter and cause a prolonged interruption of the primitive communications and accommodations serving Deep Harbor. The eastern sky was clear, the wind variable, while to the west, low on the horizon, lay sharply defined and heavy clouds, their color that of soiled and greasy cotton.

"Could snow," Sam said as the postmaster handed him the mail sack.

Sam drove his truck to Hugo's beer hall and picked up cases of empty bottles; he repeated this service at Jacques' and then at Philo's. At each stop, last minute orders were received from women who had belatedly remembered some needed article unobtainable in Deep Harbor. At last he turned the corner at the juncture and was soon spinning briskly along the curving, narrow road, hemmed in closely by the dense evergreen forest which sought to encroach upon the highway shoulders to hide the barrenness of the ugly, rocky soil.

Hugo was on the job early. This was signup day for rocking chair money and business would be brisk. Hugo needed these brisk days, for things were quiet in the woods and beer money as a result was not abundant. As he pitched a bucket of coal into the old fashioned heater, he paused to inspect the thoroughness of Beer Suds Joe's early morning job. Finding but few corners unswept, but apparently satisfied, he flipped on his radio just in time to hear the morning newscast from Channel City.

"Freezing rain turning to snow, strong northeast winds, drifting," droned the impersonal voice of the announcer. Then came a warning from the County Road Commission that highway travel would be exceedingly hazardous.

"Cripes," said Hugo to himself aloud, "them rockin' chair bosses maybe won't git here." Then, shaking his head sadly at the probable consequences to his cash register, he prepared his morning drink and moved over to a high stool behind the bar near the window affording a view of the water front area and the frozen strait reaching to Big Island.

A few snowflakes had begun to float softly earthward. Hugo knew they were wet because they flattened against the window glass and ran crazy, slithering streaks down the film of grime on the outside surface. "Come spring I'll wash 'em," was his usual rejoinder when his cronies ribbed him about his dirty windows.

Far out on the frozen straits two automobiles were slowly picking their way over the icy surface, headed for the mainland. These would be islanders, thought Hugo, coming over to sign up. He watched them wind around ice hummocks, skirt the treachery of blue patches, and finally gain the straightaway that led to the angling road below. By the time they should have reached it, they were lost to Hugo's view in the obscurity of increasing snowfall.

The Channel City broadcasting station finished a popular musical transcription and followed a commercial with a comment on the weather. Hugo listened attentively.

"Jeepers," he exclaimed, "six inches of snow up there already!" Hugo reflectively scratched his chin and stared at the loud speaker with expectance. The announcer rabbled off a message from the sponsor and then repeated the warning to motorists to stay off the highways. A further report of stranded cars and the failure of communications was interrupted by a gust of wind as the door opened and the islanders who had braved the ice bridge stumbled in with snow clinging to their clothing. Ted Crawford swished his floppy cap and sodden jacket and loudly proclaimed this to be the most nefarious winter comeback ever compounded by the Lord above and Devil below and so help him he was going to stay in Deep Harbor and drink beer until some semblance of decency prevailed in the weather. Hugo obligingly set the bottles on the bar and noted with relief that the islanders still possessed some folding money. He didn't like to serve drinks on the cuff. Then he walked to the door for a firsthand survey of the conditions outside

Ice coated the wires overhead and they sagged in festooned curves, pretty to behold but menacing in their possible consequences. Leafless trees stood resplendent in their frosty coating, while branches drooped with the weight of glistening gems. Low branched cedars and spruce hung their glazed, palm-like arms to stand like shining candy pyramids in a fairy wonderland. Everywhere it seemed that some phantom artist, tired of the dullness of all surface, had sud-

denly laid a mantle of polished silver plating to conceal its
drabness and then, to emphasize its high lights, had sprinkled it generously with diamonds. Huge white flakes fell
slowly but abundantly to the ground to form a watery mush
and then congeal into treachery and discomfort under foot.

As Hugo stepped back to close the door a frowsy amazon sloshed through the sloppy snow, excitedly waving a
postal notice of an express shipment awaiting delivery in
Channel City. Sam would be at the railway station about
now, and she wanted Hugo to telephone him to pick it up.
Hugo, who was accustomed to such requests, dutifully dialed Fairbanks where the country operator connected him
with Channel City. At best, the single iron wire afforded
but feeble audibility, and the ice coating on the communication lines in the present storm added crackles and sputters
that drove Hugo frantic in his efforts to hear and be heard.
Shouting at the top of his voice, he finally made himself understood. After a pause and a few bellowed "Hello's," the
islanders and the amazon listened with woeful incredulity
to the one sided conversation.

"You say Mr. Paris ain't there yet?"

"What's that again? I can't hear you."

"You got snow?"

"You got bad snow?"

"You say he couldn't get there in the snow?"

"You say nothin' is comin' in?"

"No trucks, no trains, no nothin'? Speak louder, please,
I can't hear you."

"Operator—operator—operator," and, after frantically
jiggling the receiver, Hugo hung up. "The phone's dead,"
he announced.

The news spread from Hugo's to Jacques' to Philo's

and to the general store. "Sam Paris didn't make Channel City," made the rounds again and again, "no milk, no beer, no groceries."

"And no rockin' chair money," added Ted Crawford as he ordered another bottle.

All that day the heavy flakes fell softly and relentlessly. No wind stirred the rhythm of their vertical descent. As the frosting of their union built into a knee deep carpet of sticky white, vehicles slogged into helpless immobility. A few folks ventured out on errands of importance. Others gathered in the beer emporiums to nurse tenderly and slowly the few bottles that their shrinking cash could afford. Conversation, always aimless in Deep Harbor, took on some animation as the possible consequences of snowbound isolation were discussed. Darkness arrived early as the feeble light failed to penetrate the opaqueness of the falling snow screen. The thermometer fell steadily to add crispness to the heavy flakes, but it in no wise diminished their abundance.

Ted Crawford and the other islanders hung around the bar making good Ted's early threat to stay in Deep Harbor and drink beer. A scant dozen of the local guzzlers straggled in. Some played cribbage; others talked about the weather and the highways. Drinking was moderate for, as Hugo feared, the rocking chair bosses did not arrive. Most of his patrons left early. The islanders, apparently too low on cash to continue drinking, and having nowhere else to go, settled themselves on the booth benches in half reclining positions.

Hugo turned off two of the three ceiling lights in a manner suggesting closing time. When he saw the islanders kick off their boots, he knew he was stuck with them for the night. Performing little inconsequential tasks be-

hind the bar to while away the time and sensing that beer
sales for the evening were over, he carefully emptied the
cash register and, as if on second thought, locked the remaining beer in his cooler. Then, after placing the poker
askew in the fire door of the stove to ease its draft, he
donned his boots and jacket, switched off the remaining
light and, pausing behind the closed outer door for his keys,
he listened for a moment to the steady snoring of his guests.
A moment later he was stumbling through the deep snow,
homeward bound.

Deep Harbor will long remember that night. In the
very early hours of the morning came the first indication of
what was to come. The temperature was a low ten. A breeze,
gentle as a tired sigh, swayed the branches slightly. The
heavily iced coating crackled softly and then all was quiet.
A few moments later, the breeze repeated its gentle probing as if to test its strength. Then unhurriedly it set its pace,
slowly at first, then increasing its velocity with stealthy deliberation. Telephone and electric wires crackled softly and
tree branches joined with metallic clicking. Then it struck
with all its fury, and the early morning darkness was hideous in the confusion of the snapping reports of tree trunks
and branches unable to support the heavy laden twigs
against the pressure of the gale. Telephone poles broke midway to add the singing rasp of ice coated wires to the clash-
ing sound, like swinging sabers, as branches, trees, and poles
creaked and rubbed in the ordeal of resistance, only to fall
in helpless disorder and travail.

The steel gray of the morning light saw but a silver
coated jumble of tangled branches, trees, and wires with the
wind stirring the now dry snow into swirling drifts in a vain
attempt to conceal the shambles. Festooned wires hung in
grotesque, shapeless patterns from the buildings and the

few trees that remained standing. It was bitter cold. The long feeble power line from Channel City had failed, and as the Deep Harbor folks awakened, only those who possessed old fashioned battery radios were able to comprehend the seriousness of their predicament. The broadcast information was gloomy. Snowplows and snowfighting equipment could not cope with the giant drifts that had isolated the northern counties from all communication. The highway department could hazard no guess as to when roads could be opened, adding the information that continuing high winds were closing in highways as rapidly as they were being cleared. The Power Cooperative warned that it would be days before service could be restored. The harsh facts of isolation come to full realization only when the implements of gracious living cease.

Blocked highways were no new experience to Deep Harbor, nor were interruptions of power service or telephone communications. By nightfall, however, when the pitifully inadequate street lights failed to perform their duty and housewives searched through neglected nooks and corners for candles and other lighting implements of yester-year, the villagers knew by the undiminished winds and the continually blowing snow that their lot would be rigorous. There would be comedy. There would be tragedy too.

The usual evening crowd gathered at Hugo's. In the dim lantern light which Hugo had managed to provide, their boisterousness was not of its usual buoyant quality. The islanders remained still, but without their earlier bombast. The villagers were buying on credit, and the postponement of payment quickened their appetites and loosened their generosity, which was especially beneficial for the stranded folks from Big Island, who munched glumly on tasteless crackers and dry cheese.

Someone asked Hugo if he had heard from Sam Paris, and Hugo, none too happy about the paucity of cash transactions, flipped his washcloth in ill humor and replied, "How the hell would I hear? You think this is a informashun beero?"

Rankling Hugo was fair game for anyone and in the absence of other diversion the remainder of the evening was spent in coarse and ribald barbs against his increasing sensitivity. Hugo put an end to it with an announcement that gained him the attention of everyone without need for repetition. "I got yust one case beer left—cash only," and with that, knowing the general exodus this startling and, it might be added, saddening announcement would cause, he began blowing out the ceiling hung lanterns and making his preparations for closing. A few moments later he buttoned up his jacket, pulled down his earlaps, placed the poker in the stove's fire door and, pausing to set the night latch, noted with satisfaction that he had gotten rid of his island guests.

"Jacques and Philo kin have dem bums," he said to himself and departed.

Morning broke over Big Island and forlorn Deep Harbor with signs of diminishing winds. There were still no lights nor telephone, and radio anonuncements encouraged no thoughts of early relief. It remained cold, and bitterness and apprehension pervaded the thoughts of the isolated villagers.

A single case of beer was not a situation to call for an early opening of a beer emporium, and thus it was noon before Hugo stirred the dying embers of his stove. He had not long to wait for customers—and news. The news was interesting: Jack Baker's wife had had her baby; Ted Bernard had broken his leg; the Bernheiser kids had the measles.

"My, my," clucked Hugo, "no doctor, no nothin' in

dis town—it's about time people got wise—could be an ep-
pydemic and no way to get to Channel City in a storm—
den what?"

Seeing cash on the counter, he plunked a couple of his
precious bottles down and expectantly awaited further news.
It was not long in arriving.

Bernard's boy had snowshoed in from Dapper's Cove
and said that the roads were blocked with drifts and fallen
trees. Struble's shack had burned down in the night and the
old man had just gotten out as the roof fell in, wearing only
his underclothing. Ted Crawford and his island friends had
had a fight at Jacques'.

"A fight," Hugo asked, "what were dem bums fightin'
about?"

"Beer," replied his informant, "Jacques only had a
coupla bottles left and Ted, he was drunk and wanted 'em."

Hugo paused in his labors and with almost tragic in-
flection he asked, "What, Jacques out of beer?"

"Yep, so is Philo."

Hugo straightened up and looked surreptitiously at the
few remaining bottles under the counter. As if to voice the
calamitous conclusion of all the thirsty villagers, he said
with deep and sincere feeling, "Dat's a hell of a note now,
isn't it?"

At the general store and post office, Tom Sanderson,
at heart a kindly man, was sitting on the counter. Jack Baker's little daughter Betty, her big blue eyes looking expectantly up at him, breathlessly announced, "We got a new
baby boy at our house."

"Well, well," said Tom, reaching into the candy
counter, "a new baby. Here, you take this to the little
fellow."

The little girl giggled as she pocketed the offering.

"Aw, he can't eat yet, only milk." She handed him a slip of paper. Tom adjusted his glasses and slowly read aloud the scrawled message: "1 loaf of bread. 1 quart of milk."

Wordlessly Tom walked through the back of the store to his living quarters. In a few moments he reappeared carrying a half a loaf of bread and a partly filled milk bottle. "You take this. We gotta wait till Sam Paris kin get through with the truck," he said, and he winced at the perplexity on the child's face.

Tom would repeat often that day, "No milk, no bread, no potatoes." And Hugo and Philo and Jacques would echo as often, "No beer, no beer."

Night fell without light, but with some hope. The battery set listeners reported the highway news. It was passed around in the beerless emporiums with great exaggeration. Highway crews told of progress, and the dejection that had possessed the serious folks of Deep Harbor lifted perceptibly. They would surely have relief by morning.

It was a happy experience for the early risers the next morning to awaken to the distant snort of diesel engines and giant bulldozers. In an atmosphere that was cold, yet clear and windless, the plight of this helpless backwoods village was painted in dazzling white and silver. From blackened chimneys, white wood smoke rose lazily in the still frosty air to render it wraithlike and unreal. Folks dressed hurriedly and from their windows watched the plumed wreath of the big rotary snowplows as they battered the deep drifts in the tamarack swamp road half a mile distant, or paused to permit the bulldozers to clear fallen trees and poles. The bright orange colored equipment was startling in its bold contrast with the ocean of white surrounding it, as it slowly worked its way to the village.

Housewives hurried to the general store to stand in

shivering expectancy, while the men gathered in little groups eagerly watching the distant progress. A happy shout greeted the first appearance of Sam Paris' bright red truck far in the rear of the battling snowplows. Those villagers who were still indoors ran out to watch the triumphant entry.

In front of Philo's, Jacques', and Hugo's and the general store and post office the crowds watched as the first big vehicle, its plow blade biting into the heavy snow, roared down the main and only street, to be followed by a second and then a third.

After what seemed an eternity, Sam Paris' truck rounded the corner and came to a stop at Hugo's. A mighty cheer went up as the men eagerly pitched in to help unload the beer cases. As it stopped next at Jacques' and then at Philo's, to be greeted by equally vociferous acclaim and assistance, the groups of women stared after it with incredulous bewilderment and dismay. Tom Sanderson watched silently and grimly. Jack Baker's little girl squirmed through the crowd to his side and, looking up at him with the frank hopefulness of childish innocence, asked, "No bread, no milk?"

Tom stooped to pat gently the shoulders of her woolly coat and, looking into her wistful, crestfallen eyes, said, "Never mind, Betty. Maybe it'll be on the next truck."

AL BERT

Apparently no one knew from where Al Bert came. Earliest memory of him went back to a decade and a half or so before the turn of the century. He was remembered then as a slender, brown haired lad of about six, of unknown parentage, a homeless waif. In those years logging flourished on Big Island, and many isolated camps were established on the shore lines. These were always temporary in nature, and their tiny populations were seldom graced by family units, especially by those with children.

Some have it that Al was simply the victim of abandonment, while others draw from their imagination to say that his parents died and in the shuffle of the roaming lumberjacks his abandonment or bereavement naturally escaped notice. Even his name seemed likely to have been a corruption. It may have originally been Albert "Somebody," later to be dignified in the form of Al Bert, which was not strange in an assembly of hard fighting, hard drinking woodsmen for whom the question of name assumed little importance.

If this was indeed his first name, his origin would be indicated as perhaps Central European immigrants, who at that period in the development of the North Country concentrated in the lower lake areas to toil in factories, or on farms, or on the spreading rail systems of the rapidly expanding Western areas. If so, his parents were no doubt a part of the very small trickle of European hopefuls that reached the forbidding shores of the Upper Lakes, there to prosper and achieve, or to end in unnamed and forgotten graves.

Al had none of the lightheartedness and playfulness of a normal child which comes from the tenderness and love of responsible and interested guardianship. He was rather like the camp dog who belonged to no one, yet appealed to the spark of human kindness ever present in the hearts of the rough, coarse toilers of the forest. He wandered about the camps always with a peculiar look of bewilderment and wonderment, and when he spoke at all it was in monosyllables accented by the nodding or shaking of his head.

He was neither shy nor bashful, nor did he shrink from human association, particularly with grown folks. His response to chow call was matter of fact, and he accepted these eating privileges apparently as his just due, the same as if he were one of the crowd.

Like the boisterous, swearing lumberjacks, Al took his turn at the washbasin dashing cold water over his face and hands; then, reaching for the camp comb dangling from a string tied to a tree trunk, he would give his shock of brown

hair a suggestion of a parting, the while peering at himself
in a mirror fragment perched on projecting shaggy bark.
Someone had thoughtfully placed a crude elevated platform before the mirror to accommodate these facilities to
his childish stature.

Where Al slept seemed to be no one's concern. Apparently he curled up and went to sleep wherever he happened
to be when the desire for sleep overtook him. This might
be on the kitchen counter or in a convenient camp bunk, or
perhaps in a woodshed or the horse barns. Whichever place
he might choose, his claim to undisturbed slumber was
never denied.

During the daylight hours when only the cooks and
the wives and children remained in the camp area, he
seemed always busy. In his unobtrusive manner he would
stare fixedly at some object that fascinated him. The spangles on a harness hanging over a hitching rail would hold
his attention for hours. Occasionally, when his wandering
would bring him into the home of a woodsman's family, he
would quietly and gravely observe such simple objects as
alarm clocks, flat irons, or perhaps a child's toy. Pictures and
firearms especially fascinated him. He would never touch
an object that caught his attention but would, for example,
spend hours examining a rifle placed within his reach, shifting his position of observation to view it from various an-
gles, always with that puzzling, inquiring look.

Housewives toiling away at the family laundry, or stirring steaming pots would turn to find Al silently watching
every movement. Though he never would indicate a longing
for some toothsome morsel, he would accept little handouts
from the kitchens with a perfunctory nod of thanks. When
he came upon other children playing, he entered not into
their youthful circles, but watched instead their movements

from aside. Pranks and antics which would cause a burst of spontaneous laughter affected him not at all.

Nor did he confine his presence to a certain camp. Frequently he would disappear for days or weeks, and his absence would arouse no curiosity or urge for search. Soon word would come that Al Bert had been seen at Burnt Point, Windy Cove, or perhaps at distant Island Bay.

That he obtained any schooling at all is doubtful. But his skill in following pathless forests to emerge unerringly at distant camps would indicate broad knowledge of nature's secrets. He studied birds, flowers, trees, and animals with the same intense absorption with which he viewed such meaningless baubles as harness spangles. He learned to set snares to catch the snowshoe rabbit As he grew older his skill in tracking and stalking contributed greatly to the camp larder.

Al learned to fashion arrows and to string bows. Once he felled a moose and needed the boss driver's help to drag the carcass to the camp site. Exclamations of adulation for this feat were accepted by him with quiet dignity and without comment. Long before reaching manhood's estate, he performed the tasks of grownups.

As always in a sparse, fluid camp population, folks came and went. Al's was a constant change of acquaintances. His welfare, training, and comforts lacked the continuity afforded by the love and affection of parents. New faces, puzzling changes of camp sites, new forest paths—all these shaped his character.

Al Bert reached maturity as he had lived his childhood —an individual quiet, unobtrusive, beholden to no one. Always there was that look as if he were peering into the future, puzzling eyes seeking understanding, the truth of things, or perhaps a reason for being. His was not a voice crying in the wilderness; his was the dignity of a human soul, striding steadfastly along an uncharted course into a life whose beginning was obscured forever from the knowledge of himself or of others, and whose ending was, like the land in which he lived, shaped by caprice, adventure, and the vagaries of men. A child of the forest fastness, he faced the inevitableness of things to come with curious anticipation, yet unafraid.

.　　.　　.

At the Northeast tip of Big Island a rocky bluff looms prominently, its sheer barren face looking out over Island Bay to the myriads of islands and the distant Canadian shores. From its boulder strewn base, a tongue of land extends in a northwesterly direction for half a mile, ending in a broken, rocky beach to form, on one side, Lost Cove and, on the other, Shelter Bay. The land was later to be called Bald Point, and for good reason.

A decade or two before the turn of the century there extended from the bluff to the beach a growth of white pine, the like of which existed nowhere in all this land. In consequence it became an early victim of the lumber companies. Then came the second growth, luxurious in its density, to conceal the scars of man's devastating greed.

But what was destined to be in later years a forest of wealth and beauty was visited by disaster. Great fires swept Big Island. For months the smoke obscured the sun and signalled to all the vast lake area the island's agony of conflagration. Timber of untold worth was destroyed before rain halted the onward sweep of total destruction. The deer and moose fled in terror to neighboring islands or perished in the path of consuming fires. When at last the skies cleared, great charred areas marred the beauty of the landscape and ghostly, blackened monarchs of the forest stood mute and leafless in the awfulness of a great catastrophe.

Hardly an area escaped the fury of the great destroyer. As if to punish it for its special beauty, the fires leaped the barriers of Lost Cove and Shelter Bay to slash with all consuming vengeance at the youthful forest on Bald Point. For many months the moss smoldered and fires crept to flare again with renewed vigor as though this bit of nature's wonderland were singled out for total annihilation. Then came the winter snows, to lay a mantle of white over the stark nakedness of desolation.

Spring came. The receding snows revealed a leafless, blackened, barren ground. Rivulets of melting snows coursed downward on the rocky slopes, and as the warmth of the spring sun increased, tiny wild flowers spread their lacy patterns over rocks and crevices and glacial drift.

The trees were gone excepting only one. Beside a path of spring dampened ground, a little pine stood, strange and alone. Slowly the light green of newly formed needles appeared on its seared and crippled branches. The first breath of summer sealed its broken bark to heal the scars of meaningless destruction. Throughout the summer it faltered as if to die, rallied, and sought again to attain a foothold, until finally the merciful winter snows again covered it with their blessed mantle of protection.

The seasons came and went. Slowly the little pine strengthened and grew, alone and without the kinship of the forest. Nature decked the nearby rocks with fresh mantles of green moss. She spun the fabric of her flowers in an ever increasing carpet of green, violet, and yellow, at the same time hiding the broken branches and scars of tragedy with newly placed growths of thick pine needles.

The turn of the century found the pine tall, graceful,

sturdy, alone—a sentinel looking out over the beauty of Island Bay and its distant shores—its branches spreading toward the sparkling waters of Lost Cove and Shelter Bay, and before it a narrow tongue of rocky, barren land extending to a jagged beach.

. . .

The logging camps moved inland on Big Island as heavy cutting thinned the timber near the shore lines. Distance complicated the methods of transportation of heavy logs to the boom assemblies, there to be floated to the distant mills.

The era of the narrow gauge railway, as it did elsewhere in the heavily timbered Northland, reached into the heart of the island. Gone was the simplicity of the axe, the saw, and the hoisting engine. Steam locomotives on narrow rails laid on precarious roadbeds now toiled to drag the heavy logs lakeward. In the woods the lumberjack still dominated the tempo of action. His cry still rang through the forest, his brawls and revelry still maintained their uninhibited quality.

Nights these forest toilers gathered around the big camp stove. There were Finns, Frenchmen, Irishmen, Poles, Scandinavians, and Southern Europeans. Tall tales, mighty oaths, heated arguments, and loud boasting mingled with the wood smoke and kerosene light to give the scene its frontier quality. In this motley and picturesque group could be found the tall figure of Al Bert, as always unobtrusive and silent, as always aside from the circle of intimacy.

Straight and tall, his brown hair flecked with gray, his countenance showing the weather beaten quality of forty odd winters, Al Bert stood aside from no man to maintain the privilege of his silence and aloneness. Newcomers, unacquainted with his quality as an adversary and seeking to invade his intimacy with provocative remarks, were stunned by the ferocity of his retaliation.

Al Bert was no saint. He had the virtues as well as the vices of his far from saintly companions. He loved, hated, fought, and drank, always with dignity and in silence, viewing the consequences of his acts with grave perplexity. He joined no festive group; when he fought, he fought alone and decisively, without anger or ill will.

He was not a fixture in any logging camp. Most of the time he worked the camps on the southern side of the island. It seemed that whenever he had been at any camp long enough to enter into the comradeship of his fellow workers, his passion to be left alone impelled him to move among stranger groups.

Frequently Al Bert left logging altogether and when he did, he would be heard of as having been seen on Big Current Island, Frenchman's Bay, or on the Canadian border. At times he would be trapping, hunting, or perhaps setting nets for fish. At other times he appeared to have no occupation. When this was the case it aroused much speculation and conjecture among his camp mates, and afforded them with an interesting topic of gossip for an evening around the camp stoves. Often this would lead into heated arguments between those who thought him queer and those who defended his independence and originality.

Logging methods in this period were also changing under the pressure of the economics of transportation and commerce. Sawmills were springing up since it was beginning to be apparent that the days of towing booms to distant mills were nearing an end.

Thus the camps became more permanent and the shipping of rough lumber, instead of rafts of logs, posed new problems. The ships that carried the forest products were larger and longer and required deeper water. Big Island responded to this by building docks and larger sawmills. And so the lumber camps lost their temporary nature and became settlements. The family units appeared more frequently and crude cabins sprang up in places that showed a remarkable diversity of preference.

All of this Al Bert viewed with bewilderment. He responded to the perplexing phenomenon by building himself a cabin. As if to protect his solitude and preserve his taciturnity, he located his cabin outside the circle of neighbors and their probable future expanding area. He placed it on a barren knoll close to the tree line behind him, but affording an unobstructed view eastward, westward, and southward over the sparkling waters of Britain Cove. Beyond lay the blue expanse of the big lake meeting the sky in a horizon of mystery and romance. Behind him lay the darkness of spruce, balsam, and cedar.

This was his first home after nearly half a century of wandering. It was small and crude, yet sturdy and substantial, reflecting, it seemed, the strangeness of his character and the ruggedness of his soul.

For a while, Al Bert appeared to have become a fixture. He would often be seen sitting before his cabin, looking out over the cove, gazing fixedly at the incoming lumber schooner rounding the channel, headed for docks laden with sawed lumber. Evenings he would watch the western skies at sunset and remain to watch the coming of the night and the stars. He worked only when his meager requirements needed the earnings.

That fall he disappeared. In midwinter, about the time when many were contemplating the acquisition of an abandoned cabin, he returned, bringing with him an Indian woman.

If the comforts of a home and love affected him, it did not reflect in Al's countenance or in his association with others. He responded to the need for increased income by working more often and steadier. His cabin outwardly showed the transition from bachelor's quarters to a family domicile. An additional wing was built, and curtains appeared in the windows. As summer came, flowers on trellises, paint on the woodwork, the familiar clothesline, and the air of neatness attested to feminine occupancy.

The cabin being remote and away from the paths of other homes, few ever saw Mrs. Bert. As might be expected, there was much speculation and tongue wagging. Her origin, like that of her husband, forever remained a mystery. Once in his presence Al was referred to as a squaw man. The frightening consequences were such that it was never repeated.

These must have been happy days for Al Bert. His purchases at the local commissary, his quickened step homeward, and the purposeful manner in everything he did were doubtlessly engendered by the love and affection of his new found companionship.

Late one evening the following winter he knocked at the door of a cabin occupied by a woman experienced in midwifery. He spoke only three words—"Can you come?"

A few hours later Al Bert gazed upon his tiny daughter, bewildered, unable to conceal his ecstasy and delight.

·   ·   ·

Up on Bald Point the late afternoon sun bathed the bluff and the great lone pine before it with a reddish light, in sharp contrast to the deep green carpet of countless pine seedlings that spread from the parent tree out to where the tongue of land ended in the now icebound, broken beach.

The lone pine no longer had the grace and beauty of its youthful growth. But what it lacked in beauty it replaced with an almost human quality of strength and ruggedness and character.

Its great crooked trunk and its gnarled, spreading branches reaching out toward Lost Cove and Shelter Bay spoke eloquently of its brave survival of the ravishes and cruelty of a tragedy half a century past.

And as the sun sank its silhouette showed sharply against the dimly lit evening sky, a sentinel guarding and protecting the newborn forest on Bald Point.

. . .

The years moved on. The lone cabin of the headland looking over Britain Bay was the scene of constant transformation. Al Bert worked hard and long to better support his cherished family. The effective bite of his axe felling the timber for the ever hungry sawmills was the theme of any evening's conversation in the bar rooms. Crew bosses vied with one another to include him on their payrolls. When mills were stocked beyond capacity and logging needed curtailment, Al Bert busied himself with other gainful pursuits but, unlike those of his earlier years, these pursuits were always near his hearth. He ran his trap lines, hunted, and fished. When not at work he was at home. When the southeast wind blew softly townward it carried with it the melodious sound of feminine laughter, of gaiety, and of happiness.

Folks remember little Lonestar Bert first as a toddling baby. Her father carried her with him often on his trips to the commissary for supplies. She would hide beneath his huge lumber jacket and with her dark and laughing eyes peep out upon the strangeness before her. Hers was always an expression of mirth and humor. As she grew older she often toddled beside him, raising her arms toward him when tiny legs proved unequal to the task of walking.

The bustling lumber town now contained an ever increasing child population. A crude one room school was erected in a grove of hemlock and somehow a teacher was obtained. There are many who can still remember the first day Lonestar walked across the threshold of the school house. Dressed in a scarlet frock, her yellow bonnet dangling from a cord about her neck, jet curls about her shoulder framing a pair of twinkling humorous eyes and a face with the delicate swarthiness of her Indian mother, her body was slender and straight with the confident, dignified poise of Al Bert.

. . .

Down *below* in the bustling factory centers the pace was feverish and often senseless. America was taking to wheels and giant factories were springing like mushrooms to supply an almost insatiable demand for family transportation. For the next several generations the automobile was to shape society and commerce, and to gear America to an assembly line. People were to toil in the dust, smoke, noise and sweat of cavernous factories. The sparkle of clear water, tiny islands, the freedom and quiet of deep cool forests, the sound of rushing rivers, the clear skies and endless distances, were the dreams of many as they bent to their tasks in the rush and roar of mass production and the pitiless pursuit of achievement and success. They sought escape in the peace and quiet of distant places and pushed northward to realize their dreams.

Many leaped the barriers of the straits to push far into hinterlands and inaccessible coves and bays, on islands and along streams and tiny lakes, some to pause briefly, others to linger and to stay. Some came to Bald Point between Lost Cove and Shelter Bay up on the northern tip of Big Island to camp and play or rest within the lovely youthful forest.

Far from the vestiges of urban conveniences, far from telephones, running water, highways, and delicatessens, they came to find the freedom and peace for their troubled dreams and respite for their suffering souls in plain crude cabins built among delightful pines, under clear skies and near soothing waters. They came to watch the setting sun cast a golden light on the sheer rock face of the bluff and on the gnarled, outstretched branches of the tall and aging pine before it.

. . .

The lumbering town on Britain Bay had reached its crest. The fast disappearing timber could no longer supply the huge sawmills. Before many years the screeching roar of great saw blades would cease, and the brief commerce that had graced Big Island would crumble and decay. Nature in her wisdom had already sown the depleted areas, and new forests followed closely the vanished pine and spruce.

The narrow railroads had already gone. On the Island were two roadways, crude, rough, and at times impassable. One led from the western end eastward to Britain Bay, another northward to Bald Point. Recreational pursuits for jaded urban visitors would slowly replace the dwindling incomes of the Island folk. Already the cabins to which they returned year after year were springing up on the coves and points and inlets that formed the shores of Island Bay. They braved the ruggedness and uncertainty of wagon trails and rocky roads to blend their hopes and pleasures with those of the weather beaten people of the Island. Their needs they purchased from the commissaries of the once busy, but now declining, lumbering settlements. They joined in the simple social pursuits of the lumberjacks and sawmill toilers, and the impact of their urban habits merged with the customs of the natives. Wherever dances, box socials, or simple local celebrations occurred, there could be found the few summer colonists whose hearts and minds inclined to accept the rigors of the Island in preference to the turmoil of the city.

As logging declined, Al Bert busied himself with other means of income. Winters he trapped and hunted; summers he fished or served the needs of tourists. The taciturnity of this aging native, his prowess on the trails, and his woodsman's knowledge fitted into their recreational pursuits and desire for adventure. Apparently he prospered and provided well the needs of his little family. His cabin on the point had the air of solidarity and security.

A lumber village at its best has always the appearance of transientness. In its inevitable decline it inflicts an air of dejection. The unmarried are first to leave and the bunkhouses, cook shacks, and other male accommodations soon take on that air of poignant wretchedess. The families, as if to stay the pangs of separation, linger on. A few indeed remain to find new occupations.

And so it was with the settlement on Britain Bay. The commissary remained to fill the needs of a growing tourist population. A handful of families who contrived a meager living in the forests and on the waters remained to become the sparse fixed population of the Island. The little school house faltered, but remained a while to perform its purpose, and then it hid its wretched destiny in a curtain of sympathetic vines and shrubs and reproducing forest.

This is a big country and the birth and passing of such episodes as the settlement on Britain Bay are but passing clouds, briefly displaying their shadows.

History will perhaps never record the destiny and purpose of Britain Bay, nor its part in the vibrant life of a nation on the threshold of its maturity. In the memories of those who, by choice or accident, now toil within the harshness of its decay, or for the love of its priceless scenic quality and the purity of its freedom dwell within its forested bowers, the story of Al Bert is inseparable from its fate.

Al Bert survived the passing of the Britain settlement. His devotion to the comforts and security of his family remained the passion of his declining years. Folks tell with brightening eyes and animation of little Lonestar, her schooling, and her ways. She retained her childish mirth and humor as she grew. Her laughing eyes and long black curls, the freshness and graciousness of her manner, the melody of her voice—all these are spoken of as though the speaker felt the magnetic stimulating quality of her presence. They tell of her childish habit of humming tiny, disconnected tunes, of singing as she trudged lightheartedly to and from her home.

They tell how on the occasion of an eighth grade school program, Lonestar sang to a parent and tourist audience with such intense feeling and vivacity that upon completion they sat spellbound, unable to applaud. And they tell how, sensing this, she swung quickly, with curls tossing and dark eyes flashing, into a rollicking lyric which provoked such laughter and applause that the program was unable to continue.

They tell also of a summer colonist of apparent wealth who, sensing the quality of her natural artistry, took an especial interest in Lonestar, and how he penetrated the

closely knit sanctity of the Al Bert home to become perhaps the only intimate. They tell with lowered voice of the
passing of Lonestar's mother, of the girl's absences during
the long winter months thereafter, of her return each summer, and of her rapid growth into womanhood.

Al Bert appeared to accept these things to be as inevitable as the passing of the seasons. He retained the dignity
of his silence and the erectness of his carriage. If sadness
over these events entered into his sturdy heart, there was
no outward sign. This strange old man well into his seventies still viewed the distant horizons, still gazed upon objects of interest with wonderment and awe. If the infirmities
of his age belabored him, it was noticeable only in the lessening of his activities.

The year appears to have escaped memory, but it was
shortly after the Christmas Holidays. The festive season
found only feeble response in the vanishing settlement on
Britain Bay that year, and the ice came early. A crimson
plane circled above the ice locked cove to come to rest in
the shelter of abandoned docks. Early the next morning the
uniformed pilot was seen assisting Al Bert aboard. The
plane departed and soon disappeared in the horizon, headed
for *below*.

In the great Motor City, amid the comfort of luxurious
surroundings, Al Bert visited his daughter Lonestar. No lux-
ury could conceal their affection for each other, nor the joy
of their reunion. That evening in the vast civic auditorium
he heard her sing and, with the superb quality of her voice,
hold an audience enthralled. The immense ovation, her
name emblazoned on the marquee of the opera house, and
the plaudits of the critics heralding the new nightingale
were beyond his comprehension. Al Bert saw only that his
daughter was happy and secure.

It was a cold February evening when he returned to his cabin on Britain Point. A few days later neighbors, seeing no smoke issuing from his chimney, found him peaceful and content in final sleep.

That day they returned him gently to the forest from which he had come.

.   .   .

Up on Bald Point dark clouds concealed the winter sunset. Brisk northeast winds swept across the frozen surface of Island Bay and the young pine forest swayed in the violence of their force. As darkness came the wind swept stronger, and drifting snows piled high in the savage fury of the storm. Below the rocky bluff a tall, gaunt pine, its gnarled branches naked of their needles, faltered, swayed, then shuddered and sank silently into the deep softness of the snow.

Next day the rising sun cast a deep morning shadow on the sheer face of the bluff; the headlands on the distant shores showed purple against the winter sky; the fresh snow glistened on the frozen waste of Island Bay and on the young pine forest stretching to the frozen, rocky beach.

THE LAST SHIP

THE ore carrier, Steamer *Iron Maiden,* nosed eastward into the late November storm. Below decks was the last shipment of ore for the mills of the lower lakes from the northernmost port of the Great Lake *above.*

Far ahead the wispy smoke plumes of two other carriers showed briefly in the steely gray overcast, and the eastern horizon blended sea and sky with the deep purple of ominously swollen clouds. Behind her lay the dark haze of the receding shore line and the foam flecked violet waters of the harbor area spiked by two converging breakwalls. Only the white coated standards of the pier headlights broke the monotony of the sullen and forbidding foreground.

A few hours ago the last of the frozen red rock ore had cascaded in a steaming avalanche into the ship's cargo hold. On the steel deck the moist earthy dust, driven by the strong easterly wind, had formed a sticky slime. The hurrying deck hands had slipped and skidded as they battened down the hatches secure against treacherous winter seas, while seamen had played the force of pressured water to flush the reddish scum through the scuppers and away.

Captain Wadsworth scanned the horizon and glanced again at the white slip of paper on which was neatly written the coded weather forecast. To the right, barely discernible, the faint outline of Indian Reef showed through the low lying frosty vapor which danced in grotesque shapes to be torn by wind into wraithlike shrouds. Nodding to the mate, he took his position on line with the jack staff. The mate placed the bearing indicator on the plate glass of the pilot house side light and the Captain gave low voiced directions to the wheelsman. The stern of the big ship swung in a steady arc. The mate nodded, the wheel spun rapidly to line, and the ship steadied and lay in her course. A short whistle blast sounded and back aft the log line whipped taut.

The wind pennant showed head winds straight on. Already the long hull dipped and rose in slow, steady cadence and the spray bounded over the bulwarks, showering the windows with noisy, insistent droplets. The ship's bell clanked the afternoon hour of two. Captain Wadsworth shrugged his shoulders and moved over to allow the mate his place, saying, "Getting dark early . . . dirty weather ahead. Going back aft for a bite and then some shut-eye . . . call me if she changes."

The deck was slippery with new ice, and the rail glistened with its frozen crust. The sea brushed the ship's hull with a slow, sibilant swish, breaking away in a welter of white hissing foam. The dense low clouds of the distant horizon widened and came nearer, and the sea turned darker.

It was hours later when the mate awakened the ship's master. "Sleet," he said, "and colder. Freshening quite a bit and to the north."

The Captain pulled a heavy turtle neck sweater over his head, crammed a visored cap over his hair, and climbed the circular stairway to the darkened pilot house. A chill breeze from the open window confirmed the lowering temperature. The glass lights were frosted. Only the glow of the radar screen broke the monotony of inky blackness. Sleet pecked at the windows and swept with stinging fragments into the pilot house. The soft swish of the bow spray was drowned out by the roar of the restless, invisible sea. From behind came the intermittent groan of the ship's whistle, repeating again and again the warning signal of blind travel.

On the radar screen the stabbing rotation of the sweep hand brought flashing lights of contact, showing the two ships far ahead. Behind there was only the filmy turbulence of a rolling sea and faint impulses reflected from the sleet and snow.

Captain Wadsworth flicked on the searchlight. The sleet in a thousand streaks of white against a background of ebony dove over the forepeak and the bulwarks glistened back. Turning off the light, he glanced at the radar screen. The mate adjusted the earphones and dialed the direction finder. The ship's bow dipped sharply and the steel hull shook with the impact of the swell. An avalanche of water swept over the bulwark, raced around the pilot house transom, over the bridge deck, and splashed noisily down the steep deck ladders. The engine, relieved momentarily from the steady drag of full wheel immersion, raced madly and the steel hull rumbled and quivered.

"No use," the Captain muttered, "lay course for the lee of Pilot Island."

The mate snapped on the hooded light over the chart table, applied the parellel rule and dividers, and spoke briefly to the Captain.

Slowly the big ship eased her precipitous plunging. The rise and fall of the stern and bow continued, but with rhythmic regularity. With the wind now quartered, the force of the sea was starboard, and it cascaded over the hatches. The rim of ice crusting the hatch combings and rails thickened by inches. As the hurricane increased its force the ship's fore structure creaked and grated. Below, unlashed objects jangled and rumbled in ominous discordance with the shrieking wind. The hissing thunder of an invisible sea in the blackness without accompanied the rat-a-tat of frozen spray beating the pilot house walls and windows.

There was yet no sign of dawn when at last the ordeal of ceaseless, terrifying vigil ended in the shelter of Pilot Island. The heavy chain slipped noisily through the hawse pipe and the anchor splashed loudly. Slowly the ship swung into her anchor.

When dawn came, sullen skies looked down upon the Iron Maiden, her black hull sheathed in ice, her jack spar crumbled athwart the bulwark. Long icicles festooned her spar stays and life line and hung in wind swept curves from her iron rails. Around her stern she carried a shroud of frost and on her deck billows of ice bridged the gap between her hatches. Clouds of frosty vapor danced about her, spinning fantastic shrouds and lending a ghostly touch of desolation. Above her the wind shrieked unabated. Afar the angry breakers lashed in seeming vengeance against the rocky shore, while the great ship chafed restlessly at anchor. Around her hull at the water line slush ice drifted and congealed.

.   .   .

Days later on the angling, snow covered road leading to the water front, a handful of the weather beaten folks of Deep Harbor stood and silently watched. It was still and bitter cold.

The winter sun lay low in the west, touching the wooded bluffs behind the village. Its low slanted rays fell on the giant hummocks of ice that rimmed the shore line of Big Island and over the snowy headlands of the strait. The *Iron Maiden*, her ice laden hull glinting brightly in the cold winter sunlight, was moving slowly through the fields of cratered slush ice southward to the deep blue of the open lake below.

Far out into the limitless sea they watched her. When at last her smoke plume lost itself in distance and darkness they turned sadly homeward. It would be a long and lonely winter here *above* before the friendly plumes of the big ships would again grace the skies on their return from their mooring berths *below*.